C000244441

Easy-to-follow
WHEAT, GLUTEN
& DAIRY-FREE RECIPES

Weight loss & diabetes friendly

By Eva Detko, PhD

Copyright © 2013 Eva Detko, PhD

Published by: Eva Detko, PhD

Photography: Peter Eccott

Printed in the United Kingdom by W&G Baird.

ISBN 978-0-9927255-0-1

The right of Eva Detko to be identified as the Author of this work has been asserted in accordance with the Copyright, Designs and Patents Act 1988 Sections 77 and 78.

All rights reserved. No part of this publication may be reproduced, stored in a retrieval system, or transmitted, in any form or by any means, electronic, mechanical, photocopying recording or otherwise, without prior permission of the copyright owner.

British Library Cataloguing-in-Publication Data
A catalogue record for this book is available from the British Library.

Every effort has been made to ensure the accuracy and quality of information in this publication. Similarly, every effort has been made by the author to include only original recipes that have not been previously copyrighted. Should any such published recipe appear in this publication, it is purely accidental and not intentional. The information and recipes in this publication are not intended, nor should anything contained herein be construed, as an attempt to give, or substitute medical advice. This publication is not a medical manual and should not to be used as a substitute for medical treatment. Professional medical advice should be obtained on personal health matters. The author accepts no legal responsibility for any personal injury or other damage arising from the use or misuse of the information and advice in this publication.

Contents

Acknowledgments

Special thank you to my wonderful partner Pete. Thank you for your continuous support and encouragement, and for being so enthusiastic about my cooking. I could not have done it without you.

I would also like to thank my family, particularly my mum. Thank you for always being there for me, believing in me and providing inspiration for some of the recipes.

Big thank you to Adam Davidson. Thank you for all your support, feedback, recipe sampling, and being a good friend.

Thank you to everybody who partook in recipe testing and sampling.

Finally, thank you to everybody who provided feedback and offered words of encouragement throughout the process of writing this book.

From the author

If you have just found out that you have wheat, gluten or dairy sensitivity, you may be feeling confused and apprehensive. There is no need. Believe me, a wheat, gluten and dairy-free diet can be very easy to follow. Moreover, there is no need to feel deprived. Quite the opposite, you can have delicious food and enjoy it. And more importantly, you may find that if you have previously had some unpleasant, medically unexplained symptoms, they may "mysteriously" disappear when you eliminate wheat, gluten and (or) dairy from your diet.

When I first discovered I was gluten-intolerant, I felt like my world was about to end. No more bread?! I did not think I could manage that. In a way, that discovery was what sparked my interest in nutrition. Seventeen years later, I have quite a different outlook. The gluten-free world is incredibly variable, and it is a great opportunity to expand your diet and explore different foods and flavours. So you can eat well, enjoy your food, and be free of nasty symptoms that interfere with your life. What is there not to like? Back in the days when gluten was a big part of my diet, I felt awful, yet apparently there was nothing wrong with me. Not what you would consider medically valid anyway. I suffered with chronic sore throats, sinusitis, fatigue, water retention, digestive disturbances (constant bloating and cramping), headaches, mood swings, and skin problems. Yet, my test results kept coming back with a note: "no action required". Wrong. There was most certainly a need to take some action. And yes, gluten was the reason for all of those unpleasant symptoms. Within a week or so of following a gluten-free diet, all the symptoms eased off, and eventually disappeared.

Over the next few years, my curiosity led me to periodically test whether I was able to tolerate gluten again. Interestingly, every time I did, most of the symptoms came back within a few days of my eating it. These days, I do not bother to test my body's response to gluten. I no longer have a need for eating gluten-based foods as I have discovered countless ways of enjoying a gluten-free diet. I have developed a new way of eating, which satisfies my taste buds, and keeps me healthy and full of energy. Apart from excluding gluten, I also choose to avoid dairy products for the reasons outlined further in this book, and because I believe my body functions much better when I do. I should add that my partner who has no special dietary requirements greatly enjoys my recipes, so they really are for the whole family, not just for those who need to have "free-from" food.

I was prompted to write this book because I see many clients who are sensitive to wheat, gluten and dairy, and I am always being asked for "free-from" recipes. I see clients across the entire sensitivity spectrum. Some people have terrible symptoms that make it very difficult for them to function. Those are the people who see the greatest improvements in their health once the problematic foods have been identified and eliminated. Others may not have debilitating symptoms, yet still find that cutting down on certain foods, and introducing more variety into their diets, boosts their energy levels and improves their mental clarity.

I also work with many clients who need to keep their blood sugar levels balanced, either because they want to lose weight, or because they have diabetes. I have found that many gluten-free cook books go a little crazy with flour. This means that the carbohydrate content of many of the recipes in those books is very high, making them unsuitable for those with diabetes or wanting to lose weight. Many of the "free-from" recipes out there are also high in fat and total calories. This is the reason why I decided to write a book that not only contains a great range of easy-to-follow wheat, gluten and dairy-free recipes, but also addresses the issue of maintaining stable blood sugar. Each recipe has been carefully designed to deliver on taste, as well as nutrition, and features a comprehensive nutritional analysis. This enables you to enjoy delicious food knowing that at the same time your meals are well-balanced nutritionally. Occasionally, you may come across a flavour combination that you may have not previously encountered or considered. I encourage you to keep an open mind and to explore those new flavours.

So here it is. Whether you are new to the world of wheat, gluten and dairy-free cooking, or just looking for some fresh ideas, I hope you enjoy using this book as much as I enjoyed creating it.

Happy cooking!

Guide to symbols

 Vegetarian

 Low calorie content (250 calories or less per serving)

 Contains a minimum of one serving of fruit or vegetables (one of your 5-A-DAY)

 Low sugar content (less than 20% of calories coming from sugar)

 Low fat content (less than 30% of calories coming from fat)

 Low salt content (less than 1 grams per serving)

 Good source of fibre (at least 5 grams per serving)

 Good source of calcium (at least 105 milligrams per serving; 15% of your daily requirement)

 Good source of magnesium (at least 45 milligrams per serving; 15% of your daily requirement)

 Good source of iron (at least 2.2 milligrams per serving; 15% of your daily requirement)

 Good source of zinc (at least 1.4 milligrams per serving; 15% of your daily requirement)

 Low estimated glycaemic load (10 or less); note that this is an estimate (refer to p. 45 for more information)

 Quick to make (30 min or less if prepared manually)

Weights and conversions

Measurements

- Both imperial and metric measurements are provided in each recipe.

- It is recommended to be consistent with the type of measurements used.

- Nutritional analysis for each recipe is based on metric measurements.

- Conversions to imperial units are approximate (rounded up or down to the nearest 0.5 oz or fl oz). This means that if this is your preferred method of measurement, you should remember that the nutritional information will not be as accurate as it would be if metric measurements were used.

- Tablespoon (tbs) and teaspoon (tsp) measurements used in the recipes are level. Due to differences in spoon sizes, cooks in Australia are advised to use 3 level teaspoons for every tablespoon listed in a recipe.

- Those wishing to use cups are advised to use cup measurements only for liquid ingredients. It is recommended to use kitchen scales for dry ingredients.

- Egg sizes specified in the recipes refer to the UK (and European) egg sizes (small: less than 53 g; medium: 53-63 g; large: 63-73 g). Note that egg sizes in the US, Australia and Canada are different. For example, medium egg in the US weighs: 50-57 g, in Canada: 49-55 g, and in Australia: 42-50 g.

Oven temperatures

Gas mark	°C	°C Fan	°F	Temperature
0.5	120	100	250	very cool
1	140	120	275	cool
2	150	130	300	cool
3	160	140	325	warm
4	180	160	350	moderate
5	190	170	375	moderately hot
6	200	180	400	fairly hot
7	220	200	425	hot
8	230	210	450	very hot
9	240	220	475	very hot

Fruits and vegetables: average weights

Item	Small	Medium	Large
Apple (whole)	75 g (2.5 oz)	115 g (4 oz)	170 g (6 oz)
Aubergine	200 g (7 oz)	280 g (10 oz)	400 g (14 oz)
Avocado	120 g (4.5 oz)	180 g (6.5 oz)	270 g (9.5 oz)
Banana (with skin)	130 g (4.5 oz)	160 g (5.5 oz)	190 g (7 oz)
Beetroot	40 g (1.5 oz)	75 g (2.5 oz)	100 g (3.5 oz)
Cabbage	600 g (21 oz)	1000 g (36 oz)	2000 g (71 oz)
Cauliflower	500 g (18 oz)	800 g (28.5 oz)	1200 g (43 oz)
Carrot	80 g (3 oz)	100 g (3.5 oz)	160 g (5.5 oz)
Celeriac	350 g (12.5 oz)	450 g (16 oz)	550 g (20 oz)
Courgette	120 g (4.5 oz)	180 g (6.5 oz)	250 g (9 oz)
Cucumber	160 g (6 oz)	250 g (9 oz)	350 g (12.5 oz)
Dried fig	17 g (0.5 oz)	20 g (0.5 oz)	24 g (1 oz)
Flat mushroom	40 g (1.5 oz)	55 g (2 oz)	65 g (2.5 oz)
Gherkin	17 g (0.5 oz)	25 g (1 oz)	35 g (1 oz)
Kiwi	70 g (2.5 oz)	90 g (3 oz)	120 g (4.5 oz)
Leek	100 g (3.5 oz)	160 g (5.5 oz)	270 g (9.5 oz)
Lemon	130 g (4.5 oz)	150 g (5.5 oz)	180 g (6.5 oz)
Mango	250 g (9 oz)	450 g (16 oz)	650 g (23 oz)
Onion	80 g (3 oz)	160 g (5.5 oz)	220 g (8 oz)
Orange	170 g (6 oz)	220 g (8 oz)	280 g (10 oz)
Parsnip	70 g (2.5 oz)	120 g (4.5 oz)	230 g (8 oz)
Passion fruit	12 g (0.5 oz)	16 g (0.5 oz)	23 g (1 oz)
Pear	100 g (3.5 oz)	150 g (5.5 oz)	250 g (9 oz)
Pepper	120 g (4.5 oz)	150 g (5.5 oz)	200 g (7 oz)
Pineapple slice (without skin)	50 g (2 oz)	65 g (2.5 oz)	80 g (3 oz)
Pomegranate	170 g (6 oz)	280 g (10 oz)	380 g (13.5 oz)
Potato	75 g (2.5 oz)	150 g (5.5 oz)	220 g (8 oz)
Sweet potato	180 g (6.5 oz)	280 g (10 oz)	400 g (14.5 oz)
Tomato	80 g (3 oz)	100 g (3.5 oz)	150 g (5.5 oz)

Please note that the nutritional information provided with each recipe is based on average UK weights of fruits and vegetables, as specified in the table on p. 9. Average weight of fruit and vegetables may vary between countries. If unsure, it is recommended to use kitchen scales.

Liquid conversions

Note that these conversions are approximates

US	Australia	Metric	Imperial
0.25 cup	0.25 cup	60 ml	2 fl oz
0.5 cup	0.5 cup	120 ml	4 fl oz
0.75 cup	0.75 cup	180 ml	6 fl oz
1 cup	1 cup	235 ml	8 fl oz
2 cups / 1 pint	2 cups	475 ml	16 fl oz
2.5 cups	1 pint	590 ml	20 fl oz
3 cups	1.25 pints	710 ml	24 fl oz
3.5 cups	1.5 pints	830 ml	28 fl oz
4 cups / 1 quart	1.75 pints	950 ml	32 fl oz

If you react to wheat or gluten

Pure oats are actually gluten-free. However, oats found on supermarket shelves tend to be cross-contaminated with other gluten-containing grains. Therefore, if you have coeliac disease, wheat allergy, gluten or wheat sensitivity, you should use oats that are certified "gluten-free". If you are amongst the small number of coeliac sufferers who react to avenin (protein found in oats), you can replace oats in the recipes with other gluten-free alternatives (refer to p. 56 for more details).

If you wish to use regular dairy products, rather than the offered dairy-free alternatives, feel free to do so but be aware that the nutritional information (including sugar, fat and calorie content, as well as the estimated glycaemic load information) may change, depending on the alternative used. If you decide to use regular dairy products, I recommend going for the reduced-fat options. I also recommend reducing the overall amount of dairy you consume for the reasons outlined in section *Good reasons to avoid dairy products* on p. 21. The best approach is to have as much variety in your diet as possible, as most food intolerances develop over a period of time due to the body being overloaded with the same food components.

If you react to dairy or lactose

If you react to dairy or lactose and do not seem to react to wheat or gluten, I would still encourage you to consider trying the grain alternatives offered in this book. The reasons for cutting down on gluten-containing grains, particularly wheat, are outlined in section *Good reasons to avoid wheat and gluten* on p. 17. If you are lactose-intolerant, you can use lactose-free products in place of the dairy-free alternatives offered, ideally choosing reduced-fat options. Be aware however, that this may affect the nutritional information provided.

If you are a vegetarian

If you are a vegetarian, you can still enjoy this book. 74 out of the 110 recipes are vegetarian, and most of those that are not can be easily adapted to suit your needs.

If you react to eggs or do not wish to eat them

If for whatever reason you do not wish to eat eggs, you can still use almost all of the recipes in this book (107 out of 110 recipes). Where egg replacers can be used, the option has been included in the recipe. For more information on which egg replacers to use and how they affect the nutritional information, refer to section *Egg replacers* on p. 58. In a small number of recipes, eggs can be omitted if necessary.

If you react to soya or do not wish to eat it

If you do not tolerate soya, or do not wish to eat it, you can still use most of the recipes in this book (101 out of 110 recipes). I have purposely used soya only sparingly, as I do not believe that soya should be consumed excessively by anyone. Where appropriate, replacement options are provided. In some recipes, soya-based ingredients can be omitted if necessary. This may alter the nutritional information.

If avoiding soya is relatively new to you, be aware of non-soya foods that contain soya ingredients. Soya bean oil, soya lecithin, hydrolysed vegetable protein, and textured vegetable protein are among the many names used to disguise soya ingredients in foods such as: breakfast cereals, chocolate, ice cream, sweets, spreads, canned produce, breads, and frozen food. It is estimated that about two-thirds of all manufactured food products contain derivatives or ingredients made from soya. Because soya is a potential food allergen, it is required by law that the label states if a product contains soya ingredients.

If you have diabetes

The nutritional information provided with each recipe enables you to track how much carbohydrate you eat, and therefore helps you keep your blood glucose levels within your target range. In order to help you achieve that, the nutritional information provided with each recipe includes: 1) the amount of carbohydrates in grams; 2) the number of carbohydrate portions (CPs), or carbohydrate exchanges; and 3) the estimated glycaemic load (GL) value (refer to section *Understanding glycaemic index and glycaemic load* on p. 45 for more information).

Please note that in this book, as accepted in the UK, one CP is equal to 10 g of carbohydrate. This is different to the equivalents in the US and Australia, where one CP is equal to 15 g of carbohydrate. The CPs in this book are adjusted for fibre content. This means that where the fibre content per serving exceeded 5 g, the number of CPs per serving was calculated by subtracting half of the fibre content from the total carbohydrate content and divided by 10.

As for the GL, it is typically recommended to aim for 100 or less per day. However, some experts agree that people with diabetes should aim even lower. All the recipes in this book have low to moderate GL values (ranging from 5 to 19 per serving). Please note, that the GL values are estimates and should be used for guideline purposes only. If you have diabetes (particularly, if it is insulin-dependent), you should not rely solely on the GL information. It is best to have a range of tools that help you monitor your carbohydrate intake. The amount of carbohydrate that is right for you depends on many things including how active you are and what, if any, medicines you take. Seek advice of a qualified practitioner if you are unsure how much carbohydrate you should consume and what method of carbohydrate monitoring may be right for you. The important thing is to follow a meal plan that is tailored to your lifestyle and helps you achieve your goals for: blood glucose, blood lipids (fats), blood pressure, and weight management. It is also important that you read information in section *Stevia and other sugar substitutes* on p. 59 before you start using the recipes in this book.

If you want to lose weight

Apart from being wheat, gluten and dairy-free, the recipes in this book are designed to enable you to keep your blood sugar stable, which is very important for weight loss. All the recipes in this book have low to moderate estimated glycaemic load (GL) values, ranging from 5 to 19 per serving. You can use this information as one of the tools to help you lose weight. It is typically recommended to aim for GL to be 100 or less per day. For more information on the importance of stable blood sugar levels and GL, refer to sections *Why is maintaining stable blood sugar so important for weight loss and good health?* on p. 44. and *Understanding glycaemic index and glycaemic load* on p. 45. The comprehensive nutritional analysis provided with each recipe also helps you monitor your intake of carbohydrates, fats and other important dietary components. Furthermore, the introduction to this cook book contains a very comprehensive list of tips for successful weight loss (refer to section *Rules of good health and successful weight management* on p. 48).

So what is the problem with wheat, gluten and dairy?

First, I would like to ask you a question. Are you familiar with any of these symptoms?

- chronic fatigue
- headaches or migraines
- gastrointestinal disturbances (bloating, abdominal cramps, gas, constipation, diarrhoea, nausea)
- Irritable Bowel Syndrome
- fibromyalgia
- cravings
- dizziness
- irrational fears or anxiety
- mood swings
- brain fog or inability to concentrate
- insomnia

- unexplained weight loss or weight gain
- aching joints or arthritis
- nutrient deficiency resulting in anaemia, dehydration, or bone density loss
- depression
- asthma
- eczema
- infertility
- irregular menstrual cycle
- muscular cramps, tingling or numbness

These are common symptoms of food intolerance. Maybe some of these problems are the reason why you picked up this book. And since you are reading this, you are probably tired of not feeling quite right, or simply feeling ill all the time. Interestingly, some people who have these symptoms choose to "learn to live with them". I know quite a few people who just put up with some of these complaints, saying: "they are not really that bad", or: "this is just the way I am". Let me tell you; these complaints are not normal. They are a sign that your body is compromised and struggling in some way. And the chances are that, if those early signals are ignored, they will probably get worse over time. On the other hand, the good news is that the body can restore itself to the state of healthy balance given the appropriate support. Of course, some of these symptoms could be due to other health problems. If they persist after you have excluded the common food irritants for a few weeks, you need to see a qualified health practitioner in order to investigate further.

Allergy vs. intolerance

It should be noted that relatively few people suffer from true allergies. Most people's symptoms are due to some level of intolerance to wheat, gluten, lactose, or other food components. A person who is allergic can react to even a very small amount of a given ingredient. In the case of a true allergy, symptoms usually come on quickly and are quite evident, e.g. swelling, rash, breathing difficulties and in extreme circumstances, an anaphylactic shock. On the other hand, symptoms of food sensitivity are more subtle and tend to take longer to occur. The symptoms are usually exacerbated by the volume and frequency of the food ingested. Some people find that they can "get away" with eating small amounts of certain foods occasionally but the moment the volume and (or) frequency is increased, the body starts producing the symptoms.

Some people suffer from coeliac disease, an autoimmune disorder in which the immune system attacks its own intestinal tissue in response to gluten ingestion. Even the smallest amount of gluten can cause a severe reaction. The consequence is wasting away of the intestinal lining and malabsorption of nutrients that leads to malnutrition. Symptoms of coeliac disease may include: anaemia, osteopenia, diarrhoea, constipation, delayed growth, arthritis, dermatitis, infertility, muscle weakness, weight loss (due to malabsorption of nutrients), and constant fatigue. Coeliac disease is usually diagnosed with blood tests and an intestinal biopsy.

Until recently, people who did not test positive for coeliac disease would be sent home by their doctors and told there is nothing wrong with them, despite displaying symptoms similar to those seen in people with coeliac disease. Fortunately, medical science is finally beginning to recognise that some people, who definitely do not have coeliac disease, still experience nasty symptoms when they consume foods that contain gluten. This type of reaction has been now termed "non-coeliac gluten sensitivity". It can closely mimic coeliac disease, which makes an accurate diagnosis a bit of a challenge. Early research suggests that non-coeliac gluten sensitivity is an innate immune response. An innate immune response is also known as non-specific immune response and is our body's first line of defence against invaders. This means that it is non-specific as to the type of organism it fights. The innate immune system, unlike the adaptive immune system, does not have an immunological memory to invading organisms and its response is not directed towards the body's own tissues. In contrast, in people with coeliac disease gluten induces both adaptive and innate immune response. The result of the adaptive immune response in people with coeliac disease is intestinal damage, as the immune system attacks its own tissue.

The number of people with non-coeliac gluten sensitivity is ever-growing. This is not very surprising considering the significant increase in gluten intake over the past 50 years, due to overconsumption of products made with highly refined wheat flour. The Western society is in a state of "gluten overload," and as a result millions of people out there have some degree of gluten sensitivity. As yet, there are no validated medical tests to diagnose non-coeliac gluten sensitivity, so an exclusion diet remains the best diagnostic tool. Eliminating gluten for a few weeks, and then gradually reintroducing it, enables you to assess your body's response to gluten.

The same way as coeliac disease and non-coeliac gluten sensitivity are two very different conditions (despite sharing many of the same symptoms), wheat sensitivity and wheat allergy are not the same. Wheat sensitivity or wheat intolerance is a delayed reaction caused by gluten (just like non-coeliac gluten sensitivity), and is not life-threatening. Whereas, wheat allergy is a true allergy. Some people refer to wheat allergy as gluten allergy, but the actual allergic reaction to wheat involves more components of wheat than just the gluten protein. So far researchers have indentified 27 different potential wheat allergens. People with a true wheat allergy tend to display symptoms almost immediately following a meal containing wheat products, or within a few hours. Symptoms are often respiratory in nature (stuffy nose, wheezing, watery eyes), but can be much more serious, i.e. difficulty breathing and anaphylactic shock. Wheat allergy is more common in children than adults. Diagnosis is made through skin prick tests, wheat-specific immunoglobulin blood testing, and a food challenge. Individuals who have gluten-related symptoms but test negative for a wheat allergy may in fact have non-coeliac gluten sensitivity. People who have been diagnosed with a true wheat allergy need to avoid foods that contain wheat ingredients. It should be pointed out that not all gluten-free foods are wheat-free. Some gluten-free products contain ingredients that are originally derived from wheat from which gluten has been removed.

When it comes to dairy allergy and lactose intolerance, again, they are not the same. A dairy allergy (milk allergy) occurs due to an adverse immune reaction to the protein in milk, casein and whey, which are normally harmless to a non-allergic individual. This affects only a small number of people. Some people are allergic only to casein or whey but most people with a dairy allergy are allergic to both. This type of reaction can occur a few minutes to a few hours following ingestion of dairy, and tends to produce symptoms such as: hives, vomiting, breathing difficulties, or, in extreme cases, anaphylactic shock.

You will sometimes hear the term "dairy intolerance". This can be quite confusing. Even though, dairy intolerance or sensitivity is also caused by an adverse immune system response, it is caused by different antibodies. However, the symptoms of dairy intolerance are not as serious as those experienced by true dairy allergy sufferers, and tend to take longer to develop. Dairy intolerance is easy to confuse with lactose intolerance, as they both tend to cause intestinal problems (stomach cramps, bloating, diarrhoea, constipation, bleeding), and in some cases nausea, headaches and fatigue. However, in addition to those symptoms, dairy intolerance can also cause an itchy skin rash, persistent cough, watery eyes, and stuffy nose. Just like with grain allergies and sensitivities, the symptoms do overlap, which can make the diagnosis tricky.

Lactose intolerance is physiologically very different from dairy intolerance or dairy allergy, as it is due to the body's inability to digest lactose (a form of sugar present in milk). This comes from insufficient production of the enzyme lactase, required to digest lactose. Unlike people with dairy intolerance, people with lactose intolerance can tolerate small amounts of dairy products. They can also have moderate amounts of dairy products to which the enzyme lactase has been added. Undigested lactose is bad news because it undergoes fermentation by the bacteria in the colon, which produces gas. Symptoms of the lower intestines, such as gas, diarrhoea, flatulence, bloating and cramps often point to some degree of lactose intolerance. However, adults who experience vomiting, burping, heartburn, or similar stomach symptoms need to look for a different root cause. Dairy allergy and dairy intolerance tend to be more common in children, whereas lactose intolerance is thought to be part of the aging process and progressive loss of ability to digest lactose. However, it should be noted that lactose intolerance can be also caused by anything that damages the intestines, such as disease, drugs, or surgery. This is known as secondary lactose intolerance.

Good reasons to avoid wheat and gluten

Since you picked up this book, the chances are you already have a good reason to want to exclude wheat and gluten from your diet. Nonetheless, here is some information to further reassure you that staying away from wheat and other grains containing gluten is a good idea. First of all, it is worth noting that gluten-containing grains (wheat, rye, barley, and triticale, which is a wheat-rye cross) are a relatively new addition to the human diet. For thousands of years, as hunters-gatherers, humans consumed a grain-free diet. Unlike ruminants (mammals that are able to digest plant-based foods), humans are not actually equipped with a digestive system that can process grains properly, and it appears that our genetic adaptation to them is not yet complete.

Wheat is the most gluten-rich grain and it is a commonly used ingredient. In fact, it is found in just about anything, from breads, breakfast cereals, pastries, and pastas to less obvious items, such as salad dressings, sauces, soups, marinades, certain brands of chocolate, yoghurts, and ice-creams. It is even used as a cheap bulking ingredient in some supplements, such as vitamin pills. Interestingly, wheat (especially whole wheat) has always been portrayed as healthy and nutritious. It must be noted that unprocessed wheat does contain certain vitamins, minerals and fibre, which give it some nutritional merit. However, it also contains gluten and gliadin proteins, which make processed wheat hard to digest, sticky and toxic (as explained below).

On balance most people could benefit from cutting down on wheat, and many people should exclude it completely from their diet. People sensitive to wheat are sometimes able to tolerate small amounts of spelt (a type of wheat also known as dinkel, or hulled wheat). However, as a general rule, most people with wheat intolerance are also sensitive to other forms of wheat, i.e. semolina, couscous (dried granules of semolina), farro, einkorn, emmet, kamut, bulgur, and durum wheat.

Other wheat and gluten-containing ingredients and products to be aware of when shopping include: brewer's yeast, bread crumbs, bread stuffing, hydrolysed wheat protein, modified wheat starch, malt, malt extract, malt syrup, malt flavouring, malt vinegar, malted milk, soya sauce, oyster sauce, matzah (traditional Jewish bread), atta (chappati flour), and fu or seitan (Asian food made from wheat gluten). Contrary to popular belief, pure oats do not contain gluten. However, the issue with most oat-based products on the market is that they are cross-contaminated with small amounts of wheat, rye or barley. For this reason, people with gluten sensitivities are advised to source oat-based products that are labelled "gluten-free". Research has shown that even people with coeliac disease are able to tolerate moderate amounts of oats. However, a very small number of coeliac sufferers have been found to react to a different protein found in oats called avenin. In those people even the purest oats could trigger an immune response.

Just to clarify, if you are sensitive to gluten, you are also sensitive to wheat. As mentioned previously, wheat sensitivity (or wheat intolerance) is a delayed reaction caused by gluten, just like non-coeliac gluten sensitivity. In this case, you might be occasionally able to tolerate small amounts of gluten without producing any symptoms. However, if you have a true wheat allergy, you will react to other components of wheat, not just gluten. Therefore, you should make sure that products you buy are labelled "wheat-free", as well as "gluten-free", as even small amounts of wheat are likely to make you feel ill.

So why is wheat and gluten so bad for you? Firstly, wheat contains a toxic substance called wheat germ agglutinin lectin (WGA lectin). Lectins are carbohydrate-binding proteins in plants that play a role in the plant's survival (nature's pesticides). Many lectins are toxic to humans. Certain lectins, such as those found in broad beans, jackfruit and mushrooms, have positive properties and have been shown to slow down the progression of colon cancer. However, it seems that most lectins present in our diet are the damaging type. When ingested, those lectins tend to accumulate in human tissues, interfering with normal biological processes. In large amounts they can damage the heart, kidneys and liver, lower blood clotting ability, destroy the lining of the intestines, and inhibit cell division. Most lectins are highly inflammatory, which means that they tend to promote inflammation in the body, as well as aggravate any existing inflammatory condition, e.g. arthritis or eczema. It should be noted that many foods, including: all grains, seeds, nuts, legumes, nightshade vegetables, and dairy, contain lectins, but in smaller quantities compared to wheat.

WGA lectin is found in all seeds of the grass family (including rye, barley and rice) but it is most concentrated in a seed of the wheat plant. Interestingly, the amount of

WGA lectin found in one slice of wheat bread could theoretically create an obstructive clot (as observed in people suffering from heart attacks and strokes), if it were injected directly into the bloodstream. Of course, this is not a likely route of exposure, but the point is that given suitable conditions even small quantities of WGA lectin could cause serious health problems. Humans have learnt to deal with the various anti-nutrients found in plants using processes such as cooking, soaking, sprouting and fermentation. Unfortunately, similarly to man-made pesticides, certain lectins are quite resistant to high temperatures, or changes in acidity levels. WGA lectin contains the same chemical bonds (disulfide bonds) as vulcanised rubber and human hair, which makes it very resistant to degradation. Lectins can be deactivated by specific carbohydrates (known as mono and oligosaccharides). Glucosamine is specific for wheat lectin, which is probably why people with arthritis aggravated by wheat (or gluten) respond to glucosamine supplementation. However, it seems more sensible to prevent inflammation and cell damage in the first place by avoiding excessive gluten consumption, than to consume gluten-containing foods and treat the resulting damage with supplements. For more information on how to deactivate lectins in your diet and reduce your exposure to other toxins, go to section *Steer away from toxins* on p. 51.

There are many other issues related to ingestion of WGA lectin. WGA lectin disrupts the body's hormonal function and interferes with appetite control mechanisms, which may contribute to weight gain. WGA lectin has been found to promote leptin resistance. Made by fat tissue, leptin is a hormone that regulates food intake and body weight. Leptin resistance is considered an important contributing factor to the development of overweight and obesity. WGA lectin has been also found to have a disruptive effect on another hormone involved in appetite control, cholecystokinin (CCK), resulting in increased appetite and impaired release of digestive enzymes. Research has shown that those who eat gluten-containing products consume on average 400 more calories per day, compared to those who avoid gluten. This higher energy intake may be also related to the fact that gluten contains opiate-like proteins (gluten exorphins and gliadorphins), which bind to opiate receptors in the brain making gluten foods addictive. Each "high" is followed by a "crush", which leads to cravings for more gluten-rich foods. This addictive nature of gluten may also be a reason why gluten tends to have a negative impact on mood and behaviour. Conditions such as: Attention Deficit Hyperactivity Disorder (ADHD), depression, anxiety, mood swings, mental fog, irritability, and schizophrenia have all been in some way connected to gluten sensitivity.

There is another reason why consuming gluten may contribute to weight problems. Gluten contains goitrogenic compounds. Goitrogens are wide-spread in nature and excessive consumption of those compounds can disrupt thyroid function. This can occur through either inducing antibodies that cross-react with the thyroid gland, or disrupting the enzyme important for thyroid hormones production (thyroid peroxidise). The disruption of thyroid function results in a sluggish metabolism, which tends to lead to weight gain, or difficulties losing weight. Goitrogens are most potent when eaten raw, and they are believed to be destroyed by heat processing. Eating small amounts of goitrogenic foods is unlikely to cause weight problems. It is the excessive consumption of gluten-containing foods that may be an issue.

Another problem is that gluten is sticky and difficult to digest. Consuming high quantities of gluten-containing foods can result in accumulation of undigested material in the intestines. This in turn tends to lead to fermentation and proliferation of the bad bacteria responsible for producing gas and toxins in the gut. The balance between good and bad bacteria is essential to intestinal health, as well as health overall. On the other hand, disrupted bacterial flora in the gut can promote yeast overgrowth (Candidiasis), which tends to have negative effects on every system and every organ in the body. Yeast overgrowth is a cause of ill health in many people. Some symptoms include: chronic fatigue, digestive disturbances, sugar cravings, food intolerances, brain fog, migraines, mood swings, poor immune function, chronic sore throat, skin problems, recurrent urinary infections, vaginal and anal itching, vaginal discharge, asthma, chronic sinusitis, weight gain, and many more.

Candidiasis is believed to be one of the main causes of gut hyperpermeability (leaky gut syndrome). Leaky gut syndrome means that larger food particles, toxins, microbes and undigested food are able to cross into the bloodstream. This can alarm the immune system and contribute to autoimmune diseases (e.g. rheumatoid arthritis, inflammatory bowel disease, type 1 diabetes, thyroid disease, lupus, psoriasis, multiple sclerosis), as well as food allergies and sensitivities. Leaky gut syndrome has been also linked to migraines, osteoporosis, asthma, autism and fibromyalgia. Leaky gut syndrome is thought to be made worse by gluten ingestion because gluten tends to poke holes in the digestive tract. Damaged intestinal lining often leads to nutrient malabsorption, which can result in vitamin and mineral deficiencies, and further health deterioration. Gluten is known to cause damage to the intestinal lining in those with coeliac disease. This is also thought to be the case in individuals with non-coeliac gluten sensitivity, although to a lesser degree.

I believe that all of the above reasons present a really good case why dietary intake of wheat and gluten should be avoided, or at the very least drastically reduced. However, there is no need to become gluten-phobic. As always, knowledge is power. Having the awareness of potential problems with gluten-containing foods enables you to make more informed dietary choices. Gluten sensitivity is a spectrum, and due to our biochemical individuality we all have different levels of tolerance to it. In my experience, many people suffering from medically unexplained complaints find that their symptoms are usually relieved by cutting gluten out of their diet. Others may find that, even though they consider themselves generally healthy, reducing gluten in their diet makes them feel more energetic and improves their physical and mental performance. As mentioned previously, gluten sensitivity is strongly connected to the frequency and volume of consumption. This is why most people who are gluten-sensitive will tolerate an occasional biscuit, or a slice of bread, but will produce symptoms if gluten is ingested regularly. Unfortunately, due to the "omnipresence" of gluten, it is not uncommon for people to have gluten-based products at most meals, or even every meal, e.g. cereal for breakfast, sandwiches or pasties for lunch, pasta or pizza for dinner, and biscuits, or other gluten-based snacks, in-between meals. Considering this, it is really not surprising that so many people these days are suffering the consequences of the toxic overload caused by wheat and gluten.

Good reasons to avoid dairy products

Whilst a true dairy allergy is quite rare, approximately 75% of the world's population is lactose intolerant. This is due to insufficient production of lactase, the enzyme essential to properly digest milk and other dairy products. Although it should be noted, that there is a significant amount of variation between races and countries. Statistics show that lactose intolerance affects approximately 95% of Asian Americans, 80-100% of Native Americans, 60-80% of African Americans, 50-80% of Hispanics, and 15% of Caucasians. From an evolutionary point of view, milk is a relatively new food for humans. Until about 10,000 years ago we were not able to drink milk as we had no animals on hand to obtain it from. Over time, some populations have developed an adaptation to the consumption of non-human milk and dairy products later in life. That adaptation is known as lactase persistence and is a result of some of our genes evolving in response to dairy consumption (mutation of the lactase gene). This mutation developed mostly in populations that had domesticated cattle and is the generally accepted explanation for the large proportion of the population in Northern Europe being lactose persistent. The process of gene mutation however, is very slow and complicated. Considering the fact that the majority of people around the world remain lactose intolerant, we still have a long way to go before we can talk about complete adaptation.

When you think about it, this is in fact quite natural and logical. Since the only function of lactase is the digestion of lactose in milk, most mammals experience a dramatic drop in lactase levels after weaning. As a species, we are no exception.

The majority of humans naturally stop producing significant amounts of lactase between the ages of about two and seven. It is as though, from the nature's point of view, we no longer have a need for it. Yet somehow, we adopted the habit of drinking cow's milk. Although there is no argument that cow's milk is an excellent nutrient source for calves, unlike humans, once calves are weaned, they do not drink milk again. If we believe that other animals' milk is so good for us, why do we not milk our cats and dogs too? That sounds somewhat disturbing, does it not? So why do we feel quite so differently about drinking cow's milk? It is because we have been brainwashed into believing that drinking cow's milk can benefit us. However, a growing body of research appears to be pointing us in a different direction.

Drinking milk has always been portrayed as essential for sufficient calcium intake in order to build strong bones in children and prevent osteoporosis in older people. However, there is substantial scientific evidence suggesting that milk consumption does not improve bone density in children and it has no protective effect on fracture risk in adults. Some clinical research shows that not only do dairy products provide little or no benefit to bone health, but excessive dairy consumption can actually contribute to developing osteoporosis and more than double the risk of stress fractures. It has been observed that countries where large amounts of dairy products are consumed suffer from the highest risk of fractures and worst bone health. Conversely, people with the healthiest bones are those who come from countries and tribes with very low or no dairy intake. One of the reasons for this phenomenon is the fact that cow's milk contains on average three to four times more protein than human milk, which makes it more acidic. The acid-alkaline balance in the body is tightly regulated. When the body's environment becomes too acidic, due to dietary or other reasons, one of the ways in which that balance can be restored is by using calcium to neutralise the excess acid. When the blood levels of calcium are insufficient, calcium is released from the bones. This is a very important mechanism because excess acid in the body can lead to metabolic acidosis, which can have very serious consequences, including coma and death. When the body becomes too acidic, the priority for the body is to recover the acid-alkaline balance to protect the brain and other organs. The risk of fractures due to compromised bone density is a secondary issue at that point. It should be noted that excessive consumption of carbonated drinks, meat and other protein-rich foods will have the same negative effect on bone health.

Numerous studies have shown that, even though bone health is partially determined genetically, we can dramatically decrease the risk of osteoporosis and fractures by: taking regular exercise, increasing our intake of vegetables and fruits, reducing the amount of toxic exposure (including: smoking, drug taking, pesticides in food and drink, and perfumed body care products), reducing the amount of dietary sodium, as well as ensuring adequate intake of vitamin D, vitamin K and calcium from sources other than dairy (more details in section *Calcium* on p. 26).

There is another potential problem with excessive dairy consumption. Cow's milk proteins contain high amounts of branched-chain amino acids (BCAAs), which when ingested cause exaggerated increase in insulin levels. This in turn stimulates production of insulin-like growth factor (IGF-1), a hormone that plays an important role in childhood growth. Although IGF-1 is vital to human health, there is a growing body of evidence that it may be linked to breast and prostate cancer. Another group of hormones under scrutiny are oestrogens. Oestrogens are primary female reproductive hormones. Normally, men have considerably lower levels of oestrogens in their bodies than women. However, certain factors can contribute to excess oestrogen levels in both men and women. This can have serious health consequences due to the ability of oestrogens to influence cell proliferation. High concentrations of oestrogens (and their metabolites) are considered a risk factor for prostate, breast and ovarian cancers. Milk that comes from pregnant cows has a particularly high concentration of oestrogens. Some researchers believe that the chronic elevated levels of IGF-1, coupled with constant exposure to oestrogens found in cow's milk, are responsible for the observed association between high dairy consumption and increased risk of cancers in Western societies. However, some others do not support this view. Higher incidence of ovarian cancer in women consuming large amounts of dairy products may also be associated with the dairy sugar galactose, that might be toxic to ovarian cells.

Apart from increased risk of cancers, excess oestrogen (oestrogen dominance) tends to lead to weight gain, or difficulties losing weight. Unfortunately, overloading our bodies with oestrogens is not hard. We are constantly exposed to oestrogenic compounds through: foods and drink (containing toxic pesticides, herbicides, and growth hormones), drugs and hormone pills (birth control and hormone replacement), cleaning products, body lotions, etc. Often people find themselves in a vicious cycle because excess oestrogen leads to weight gain and our body's fat cells also produce oestrogen. More fat tissue leads to higher circulating levels of oestrogens, and therefore further weight gain. More weight gain can also lead to insulin resistance, which leads to more weight gain and yet more oestrogen. Other potential symptoms and consequences of oestrogen dominance include: premenstrual syndrome (PMS), fatigue, headaches, acne, gall bladder disease, infertility, endometriosis, breast and ovarian cysts.

Apart from IGF-1 and oestrogens, there are other hormones naturally present in milk, produced by a cow's body. This includes growth hormone and other growth factors, which promote cell proliferation and are responsible for making calves grow fast. According to certain sources, the amount of growth hormone in cow's milk is "relatively small". However, when you think about how long it takes a calf to reach adult size, compared to how long it takes a human, you have to wonder just how concentrated the hormones in cow's milk have to be? At twelve months of age, the weight of a calf can be seven to eight times that of its birth weight (depending on the breed), whereas the weight of a human tends to be only about three times higher. Intensive farming had led to the development of the synthetic version of bovine growth hormone (recombinant bovine growth hormone; rBGH), which was then banned in Europe, Canada, Australia, New Zealand, Japan and Israel by the year 2000. In the US, public opinion has led some manufacturers and retailers to market only milk that is rBGH-free, but this is not a legal requirement. This means that products of the US origin containing dairy cannot be guaranteed to be rBGH-free. Certain sources insist that bovine growth hormone, natural or synthetic, is not active in humans and therefore unlikely to cause any adverse health effects. However, as no longitudinal studies have been conducted with regard to safety of ingesting bovine hormones, nobody can really say with certainty that these hormonal residues have no negative effects on human health.

In addition to that, intensive farming means that cows are required to produce unnaturally large quantities of milk, which is one of the reason for high incidence of mastitis in dairy cows (inflammation of cows' mammary glands). Treatment of mastitis requires the use of antibiotics, traces of which have been known to end up in milk marketed as fit for human consumption. If this were not bad enough, pesticides, polychlorinated biphenyls (PCBs), dioxins, and pus have also been previously found in milk. When these toxins accumulate in our bodies, they compromise the function of every organ and system, particularly the immune, reproductive, and central nervous system. This is one of the reasons why PCBs and dioxins have been linked to cancer. Finally, let us not forget about lectins, which tend to be present in milk when cows are fed grains rather than grass. Dairy-based lectins have been linked to increased susceptibility to type 1 diabetes (insulin-dependent) in children.

Another problem with hormones and antibiotics present in milk is that they encourage overgrowth of yeast bacteria in the gut, which can result in candidiasis and leaky gut syndrome. As explained previously, leaky gut syndrome occurs when the intestinal lining becomes damaged, allowing larger food particles, toxins, microbes and undigested food to cross into the bloodstream. As many people are unable to digest dairy properly, they are likely to end up with undigested material in their gut. This can trigger an inflammatory immune system response, resulting in mucus formation. This is why people suffering from rheumatoid arthritis, migraines, asthma, IBS, eczema, sinusitis, ear infections and many other conditions can often alleviate their symptoms by eliminating dairy products (and other irritants) from their diets. As well as being a source of contaminants, dairy products are also a major source of saturated fat in the Western diet. People consuming high amounts of saturated fat have a higher risk of developing heart disease, obesity and other serious health problems. Even reduced-fat dairy foods are becoming an issue. Because they are considered "healthier", many people seem to think it is acceptable to have greater quantities of those foods. However, the fat and the energy content soon add up. Reduced-fat milk is currently the seventh leading source of calories among Americans of ages 2 to 18. Across the Western world, high levels of consumption of milk proteins, sugar and fat pose health risks to children, encouraging the development of obesity, diabetes, and heart disease. This is not helped by the fact that casein, the most abundant protein in cow's milk, breaks down in the stomach to produce casomorphins, which have an opioid effect on our bodies. This makes dairy products addictive. Casomorphins are found in particularly high concentrations in semi-hard and mould cheeses.

If your symptoms are caused by a dairy allergy or lactose sensitivity, apart from avoiding milk (whole, semi-skimmed and skimmed), cheese, yoghurt, cream, dairy ice-cream and butter, you should pay attention to labels. Some of the less obvious foods containing dairy ingredients include: sauces, soups, salad dressings, dried mixes (cakes, pancakes, cookies, etc.), processed meats, sweets, breads and baked goods, processed breakfast cereals, instant potatoes, breakfast drinks, health supplements, many prescription and over-the-counter drugs. Check labels for the following ingredients: curd, whey, casein, caseinates (in the form of: calcium, potas-sium, sodium, magnesium, and ammonium), rennet casein, ghee, hydrosylates, lac-tose, lactulose, lactalbumin, lactoglobulin.

Similarly to wheat and gluten, there is no need to be dairy-phobic. If you are lactose intolerant you may be able to tolerate small amounts of dairy products. Again, you need to experiment with different amounts to establish where you are on the dairy sensitivity spectrum. Many people who are lactose intolerant are able to consume goat's milk (and cheese), probably due to its greater degree of digestibility. Some people choose to buy dairy products to which the enzyme lactase has been added, or take digestive enzymes when they eat dairy. Whichever option you choose, it is worth keeping in mind that in order to avoid the contaminants present in cow's milk, as discussed earlier, you need to buy organic dairy products. It should be noted that despite all the evidence, there is some fierce opposition from "dairy fans" who claim that there is nothing wrong with humans consuming dairy and that most of the research pointing towards potential problems caused by excessive dairy consumption is flawed. As usual, I encourage you to have your own opinion based on your own research and your personal experiences and symptoms.

So am I able to have a well-balanced diet if I avoid wheat, gluten, and dairy?

The answer is: **absolutely yes**. If you ever hear otherwise, please be reassured that it is complete nonsense. There are many more gluten-free grains than there are gluten-containing grains, and they tend to be more nutrient-rich anyway. And when it comes to dairy, as discussed previously, there is nothing in it that you could not obtain from a well-balanced dairy-free diet.

In fact, people avoiding foods containing wheat, gluten and dairy (e.g. cakes, biscuits, pastries, processed breakfast cereals, cheese) tend to have healthier diets because they usually eat more unprocessed foods and automatically reduce their intake of saturated fat, sugar, and salt. However, this is not the case when people consume excessive amounts of processed gluten-free foods. Those foods are often high in saturated fat, sugar and salt, and low in fibre. They can negatively affect blood sugar and trigger cravings leading to weight gain, or difficulties losing weight.

So let us have a look at the key dietary components that are important to good health and successful weight management, and how to obtain them from a gluten, wheat and dairy-free diet.

Carbohydrates

Carbohydrates are an important source of energy. All digestible carbohydrates we eat are ultimately converted into glucose in the body. Glucose provides fuel for all body tissues, especially the brain. Maintaining stable blood glucose levels is vital for successful weight management and good health in general (more information in sections: *Why is maintaining stable blood sugar so important for weight loss and good health?* on p. 44. and *Understanding glycaemic index and glycaemic load* on p. 45).

Most dietary carbohydrate is derived from sugars (e.g. table sugar, honey, jam, preserves, sweets, biscuits, milk, fruit, fruit juices,) and starches (e.g. grains, root vegetables, legumes). Sugars coming from sources any other than fruit are best avoided, or reduced to the minimum, as their nutritional value is very limited. Moreover, excessive consumption of sugary foods contributes to obesity and other health problems. Starchy carbohydrate sources tend to be more nutritious, although it depends on the way in which they are processed. Nutritional merits of refined flours are poor. Despite their higher nutritional value, fruit and unprocessed starchy carbohydrates need to be consumed in moderation by people wanting to lose weight, or those with diabetes. This is a very important aspect of this book and is expanded on in the sections specified above.

When it comes to wheat-free and gluten-free carbohydrate sources, there are many good nutritious alternatives. All root vegetables and pulses are naturally gluten-free. As for gluten-free grain alternatives, the most popular ones include: quinoa, amaranth, millet, pure oats (labelled "gluten-free"), buckwheat (no relation to wheat), rice (brown rice is a better option), sorghum, tapioca, corn and teff.

Proteins

Protein is a major component of body tissues. In addition to their structural role, proteins are also crucial for enzymatic functions (all enzymes are proteins), transport (acting as carriers for nutrients and molecules), hormonal function (e.g. insulin and thyroid hormones are proteins), immune function (antibodies are proteins), and maintenance of acid-alkaline balance. Proteins can also be used as an energy source.

Proteins consist of building blocks called amino acids, some of which can be made in the body (non-essential), while some others have to be provided by the diet (essential). Essential amino acids are found mainly in protein of animal origin (meat, fish, shellfish, eggs, dairy). Nearly all foods contain all amino acids in some quantities. However, some plant-based foods are deficient in one or more of the essential amino acids. This does not mean that you have to eat great quantities of animal protein to meet your essential amino acids requirements - far from it. There are some plant-based, gluten-free foods that contain all of the essential amino acids, e.g. quinoa, amaranth, buckwheat, hempseed, chia, soya, spirulina. Moreover, mixing different plant-based foods, which occurs at most meals, ensures a better amino acid profile. In summary, it is perfectly possible to have a gluten and dairy-free diet and consume enough protein, provided that the diet is variable. The same applies to vegetarians. In actual fact, most people consume more protein than their bodies require, which is not a good thing. The dangers of acidosis have already been discussed in section *Good reasons to avoid dairy products* on p. 21.

Fats

Fats are found in all the cells in our bodies and are the most concentrated form of dietary energy. Fats supply fuel for cells and transport fat-soluble nutrients in the bloodstream. They provide insulation against heat loss, and mechanical protection for internal organs. Fats provide material for making hormones and other molecules. They are also the main components of cell membranes. The working surface of the brain, as well as large proportion of the sheath surrounding nerves is made of fat.

Dietary fats are divided into saturated and unsaturated fatty acids. Saturated fatty acids are predominantly obtained from products of animal origin (e.g. fatty meat, lard, dripping, full-fat dairy products). Saturated fats are also found in foods of plant origin (e.g. seeds and nuts), but in much lower quantities. Excessive intake of foods rich in saturated fatty acids can lead to obesity, cardiovascular disease, diabetes, fatty liver disease, and other serious health problems. Saturated fat is widely spread in the Western diet. With high intakes of cakes, biscuits, chocolate, fried foods, etc., most people consume far too much saturated fat.

It should be noted that not all saturated fats are equal. A very good example of this is coconut oil. It was once believed that because of its high saturated fat content, coconut oil should have the same artery-clogging, cholesterol-raising properties as saturated fat found in butter, lard or fatty meat. This is very far from the truth, and in fact the scientific evidence supporting the great health benefits of coconut oil is ever-growing. Coconut oil contains special fats called medium chain triglycerides (MCTs): lauric, capric and caprilic acid. Studies have shown that intake of coconut oil can help our bodies fight various viruses and bacteria, including yeast bacteria in the gut. Coconut oil can also positively affect our hormones. For example, it can improve the thyroid function, which helps stimulate metabolism. It can also help improve insulin sensitivity, which helps with blood sugar control. Both are very important for successful weight management. Coconut oil also improves digestion, slows down the aging process, and works wonders for skin and hair. This is good news for people on dairy-free diets, as coconut oil, as well as coconut cream and milk, are often used as substitutes for butter and other dairy products.

In terms of unsaturated fatty acids, there are monounsaturated fatty acids (MUFAs) and polyunsaturated fatty acids (PUFAs). Common sources of MUFAs include: olive, canola, and sunflower oil, olives, avocados, seeds, nuts, and red meat. In moderation they are considered beneficial to health, as they have been found to be protective against cardiovascular disease and diabetes. When it comes to PUFAs, they are further divided into omega-6 and omega-3 fatty acids. Some common sources of omega-6 fatty acids include: sunflower, safflower, corn, canola and walnut oil, as well as nuts and seeds. We get our omega-3 fatty acids predominantly from fish oils (e.g. salmon, mackerel, sardines, herring), but also edible seaweed, certain vegetable oils, seeds and nuts.

The problem is that two very important omega-3 fatty acids (eicosapentaenoic acid - EPA and docosahexaenoic acid - DHA) rely on the body's ability to produce them using yet another omega-3 fatty acid (alpha-linolenic acid - ALA). The body's ability to do that however is quite limited, particularly as we get older. EPA and DHA have many important functions: anti-inflammatory effect, cardiovascular and nervous system support, inhibition of cancerous cell growth. It is therefore crucial that we consume the right amounts of EPA and DHA.

Many people believe that they can obtain enough omega-3 fatty acids by eating vast quantities of seeds and nuts (e.g. flaxseed, chia seeds, walnuts, etc.), or their oils. Unfortunately relying exclusively on those plant sources for obtaining enough EPA and DHA is unlikely to satisfy the body's requirements. This is because the omega-3 fatty acid found in seeds, nuts and vegetable oils is ALA. The body's limited ability to convert ALA into EPA and DHA means that even high intakes of ALA are unlikely to provide us with sufficient quantities of EPA and DHA. Obtaining enough EPA and DHA can be achieved through eating more oily fish (at least twice a week) and edible seaweed (e.g. wakame, nori, hijiki and arame) which you can add to your soups, salads and other savoury dishes. If you choose to supplement with fatty acids, I advise going for a good quality EPA/DHA supplement (cold-pressed) and store it in the fridge to prevent harmful degradation.

Another problem with our fatty acid intake is the ratio of omega-6 to omega-3. The ratio is very important to get right. This is because omega-6 fatty acids can be pro-inflammatory (promoting inflammation), depending on the way in which they are metabolised. Omega-6 fatty acids are much more wide-spread in the Western diet. Generally, the ratio of omega-6 to omega-3 in Western countries is estimated to be between 15:1 and 17:1, which is very far from ideal. Many experts attribute the high prevalence of chronic illnesses in the Western world to excessive consumption of omega-6 fatty acids. Several sources of information suggest that humans evolved on a diet with a ratio of omega-6 to omega-3 fatty acids of approximately 1:1. Research has shown a ratio of 4:1 to be associated with a 70% decrease in total mortality from cardiovascular disease. However, it took a ratio of 2.5:1 to reduce rectal cell proliferation in patients with colorectal cancer. Lower omega-6 to omega-3 ratios have also been shown to have a beneficial effect on patients with breast cancer, asthma, as well as rheumatoid arthritis and other inflammatory conditions.

At this point I have to emphasise that unsaturated fatty acids are chemically unstable and are therefore easily damaged (oxidised) by heat, light or exposure to air. MUFAs are more chemically stable than PUFAs, but they are still prone to oxidation. Ingestion of fatty acids that are oxidised can result in cell damage and inflammation, potentially leading to many serious health problems. Although olive oil has been portrayed in the media as healthy, this does not extend to cooking. The main component of olive oil is MUFAs, which when heated become oxidised and toxic, resulting in formation of carcinogens and mutagens. PUFAs are even more easily oxidised and form much higher amounts of toxic lipid peroxides than saturated fats or MUFAs. This can cause your health more harm than good. For that reason, oils such as: sunflower, safflower, canola, corn, peanut, walnut, Brazil nut, sesame, pumpkin, pecan, pistachio, cashew, pine nut, almond, hazelnut (filbert), soya bean, rice bran, flax, chia, hemp, and grape seed oil should not be used for cooking. They can be added to cold food (e.g. drizzled on salads), or once the food has been cooked. Avocado, almond, macadamia, and olive oil can be used for baking and quick cooking on low heat, but should not be used for cooking at medium or high temperatures, e.g. frying. Cooking oils sprays (e.g. sunflower or olive oil spray) can be used sparingly. Cooking oils are emulsified oils and the idea is that you only use a very small amount to ensure a non-stick surface when cooking, grilling, baking, etc. Some of those sprays contain soya lecithin as an emulsifying agent, so those wishing to avoid soya should source a soya-free version.

Similarly, nuts and seeds high in omega-3 fatty acids should be treated with caution. Eating moderate amounts of seeds and nuts is fine, but they should ideally be eaten raw and never when they have gone rancid. Soaking nuts and seeds before eating them is meant to reduce the phytate and lectin content. The opinion is divided to what extent that occurs but any reduction in those compounds makes nuts and seeds healthier for us to eat. There is a great deal of contradictory information out there with regards seeds and nuts: are they good for us or are they not? On the one hand, they are full of vitamins, minerals and fibre. On the other hand, they contain lectins and phytates, and most of them have an undesirable omega-6 to omega-3 ratio. The truth is that if you look long enough, you can find something wrong with just about any food. The key word here as usual is moderation, i.e. rather than overload with selected ingredients, eat a wide variety of foods.

Fatty acids in nuts and seeds tend to suffer slightly less degradation from heating compared to oils. Researchers believe that this is because they are not as isolated as fatty acids in oils. Instead they are in a matrix of other compounds that may provide a form of protective barrier against heat degradation. Nonetheless, when cooking with nuts it is advised not to do so too frequently, and choose cashews, macadamias, hazelnuts, almonds or pistachios. Pecans and peanuts are less ideal, and it is probably best not to cook with walnuts.

Most experts in the field agree that the best oil for cooking at medium to high temperatures is coconut oil, as it is quite resistant to heat damage. You should be aware that coconut oil can vary widely in terms of the variety of coconuts used and the type of processing, which might affect the health benefits of the oil. Most commercial coconut oils contain chemicals as a result of refining, bleaching and deodorising. It is recommended to source organic virgin coconut oil to ensure the right quality. Desiccated coconut, coconut milk and cream can also be used for cooking and baking without any concerns of heat damage. Cocoa butter, lard, goose and duck fat are other dairy-free options suitable for high-temperature cooking, but only small amounts of these should be used. Although it used to be considered an "evil" ingredient, as it is predominantly saturated fat, lard is now making a comeback, as people become more aware of the dangers of consuming trans-fats. Those who do not follow a dairy-free diet can also use small amounts of butter or ghee for high-temperature cooking. Ghee can be also sourced casein-free. All of those ingredients should be ideally sourced organic, as their non-organic versions tend to contain trans fats (as a result of processing), as well as contaminants, including PCBs.

Trans fats are formed when manufacturers turn liquid oils into solid fats (e.g. margarine). This is achieved via a process called hydrogenation, in which vegetable oils are converted to solid fats by adding hydrogen atoms to the fat molecules. Hydrogenation increases the shelf life and stabilises the flavour of foods. Unfortunately, at the same time hydrogenated fats (trans fats) are very bad for our health and therefore should be avoided completely. Trans fats were originally developed to provide a "healthier" alternative for saturated fat. Luckily, researchers started questioning the safety of trans fats and eventually agreed that they are in fact even more damaging than saturated fat. Not only do they clog our arteries, increasing the risk of heart attack and stroke, but are also believed to increase the risk of diabetes and depressive disorders. In addition, trans fats interfere with liver function as they are more difficult for the liver to process compared to other fats. Excessive consumption of foods containing trans fats tends to lead to accumulation of abdominal fat, and even redistribution of existing fat to the abdominal area.

Apart from margarine, trans fats can be found in vegetable shortening, crackers (even those healthy sounding ones), cereals, sweets, cakes, biscuits, cookies, granola bars, muffins, pie crusts, pizza dough, some breads (e.g. hamburger buns), cake and pancake mixes, chips, crisps, salad dressings, fried foods, and many other processed foods. Trans fatty acids are found naturally in very small quantities in some foods including beef, pork, lamb, and dairy products, but the majority of trans fats in the diet comes from hydrogenated foods. When checking labels, look out for "partially hydrogenated" fats, as any oil that is partially hydrogenated is also a trans fat. The only way you can be sure that the product does not contain trans fats is when the packaging states "no hydrogenated fats".

In summary:
- reduce your intake of saturated fats (you can use coconut oil in moderation)
- reduce consumption of omega-6 fatty acids (i.e. oils, seeds and nuts)
- ensure sufficient intake of EPA and DHA: eat oily fish at least twice a week and include edible seaweed in your diet
- buy oils that are cold-pressed, in dark glass bottles
- store oils in cool, dark places, ideally the fridge (most oils partially solidify on refrigeration but will return to liquid form once removed from the fridge)
- avoid products containing hydrogenated or refined oils

- avoid using blended vegetable oils as they are usually a mixture of unidentified oils that have been extracted with chemicals
- do not eat oils, nuts, or seeds that have gone rancid
- avoid heating unstable oils, or consuming food cooked in them when you eat out.

Dietary fibre

Dietary fibre (or non-starch polysaccharide) is a very important part of a balanced diet. It normalises bowel movement by increasing stool weight and size, and helps optimise bowel transit time. Sufficient fibre intake is a key factor in maintaining healthy bowel function. Fibre also plays an important role in regulating blood sugar and cholesterol levels, and it may help reduce blood pressure and inflammation. Additionally, fibre is important for successful weight management as fibre-rich foods tend to be less "energy dense," and they help us stay full for longer.

In terms of its solubility, fibre is divided into "soluble" and "insoluble". Both types of fibre are present in many gluten and wheat-free foods. This means that you should be able to meet your fibre requirements without any problems, provided that you choose unprocessed foods. Gluten and wheat-free fibre sources include: legumes, gluten-free grains (e.g. quinoa, amaranth, oats), vegetables, fruits, nuts and seeds.

Most people in the Western world do not have enough fibre in their diets. This is mostly due to excessive consumption of processed foods that tend to contain very little or no fibre. The consequences of not having enough fibre in the diet include: constipation, weight gain (or difficulties losing weight), increased risk of diabetes, colon cancer, diverticular and cardiovascular disease. It should be emphasised that having too much fibre in the diet can result in micronutrient deficiencies. This is because some fibre fractions (especially phytates) bind minerals such as: zinc magnesium, calcium and iron. The British Nutrition Foundation recommends that adults should consume 18 g of fibre per day. The recommendation of the United States National Academy of Sciences (Institute of Medicine) is somewhat higher: 38 g for men and 25 g for women aged 50 and younger, and 30 g for men and 21 g for women over 51 years of age. If you think that your fibre intake is insufficient, increase it gradually to allow your digestive system to adapt to the change. Otherwise, you may experience symptoms of abdominal distension and discomfort.

Vitamin A

Vitamin A is important for growth and development, good vision and health of the immune system. Vitamin A is an important antioxidant and helps protect cells from oxidative stress. Oxidative stress results when there are more free radicals (highly chemically reactive oxygen species) in the human body than antioxidants. Some of the conditions linked to oxidative stress include: diabetes, cardiovascular disease, hypertension, and chronic inflammatory diseases. We age as a result of accumulation of free radical damage over time.

Vitamin A in our diet can be found in two forms, retinol (active form absorbed readily by the body) and carotenes (provitamin A; require conversion to retinol before the body can utilise them). The most concentrated sources of retinol include: liver, kidney, offal (and their products), oily fish, and eggs. Carotenes are found in all green, yellow, orange and red vegetables, and fruit, with the most concentrated sources being: carrots, red peppers, spinach, broccoli, and tomatoes.

The conversion rate of carotenes to retinol is relatively low [approx. 12 micrograms (µg) to 1]. This varies from person to person and is dependent on bioavailability of carotene and presence of fat, which is necessary for the conversion. Excessive regular intakes of retinol from supplements and dietary sources can cause liver damage, as retinol is fat soluble and any excess accumulates in the body. Pregnant woman should be particularly aware of high intakes of retinol, as it is potentially teratogenic (can cause birth defects). Carotenes produce no toxicity in humans as they are water soluble, which means that any excess can be excreted by the body.

Vitamin D

Vitamin D refers to a group of fat-soluble compounds responsible for enhancing intestinal absorption of calcium and phosphate. Insufficient intake of vitamin D is linked to osteoporosis and osteomalacia (rickets in children). Apart from bone health, vitamin D has been shown to support immune function, and may reduce risk of developing cardiovascular disease and multiple sclerosis.

Vitamin D is not a vitamin in a strict sense, as it can be synthesised in adequate amounts when the body is exposed to sunlight. Technically, vitamins are compounds that cannot be synthesised in sufficient quantities by the body, and therefore must be obtained from the diet. Even though many people associate vitamin D with dairy products, those who avoid dairy products can obtain sufficient amounts of vitamin D from other food sources and through exposure to sunlight. As little as 10-15 minutes of sunlight per day can satisfy the body's requirements for vitamin D. This is dependent on the individual's skin tone. Darker skin tones require longer exposure to the sun in order to obtain adequate levels of vitamin D, compared to lighter complexions. Good dietary sources of vitamin D include eggs, liver, oily fish and meat. Some brands of gluten-free cereals (e.g. corn flakes), as well as almond and rice milk, are fortified with vitamin D. Similarly to retinol, vitamin D is fat-soluble and therefore excessive intakes can lead to toxicity.

Vitamin E

Vitamin E refers to a group of fat-soluble compounds that include both tocopherols and tocotrienols. As a fat-soluble antioxidant, vitamin E plays a major role in protecting fat-containing structures, such as cell membranes and unsaturated fatty acids, from oxidative damage. Vitamin E works together with other nutrients that prevent oxygen molecules from becoming too reactive (vitamin C, vitamin A, selenium, manganese, glutathione, and others). Vitamin E deficiency has been linked to impaired immune function, poor skin health, cardiovascular disease, cataracts, neurological disorders, and red blood cell destruction.

Gluten and wheat-free dietary sources of vitamin E include sunflower, safflower, avocado, almond, and walnut oil, nuts, seeds, avocados, and green leafy vegetables. Vitamin E does not tend to be toxic when obtained from food sources alone, even in large quantities. However, vitamin E supplements, when taken in very high doses of 3000 IU (international units), or more, have been shown to have toxic effects. Symptoms of toxicity include: intestinal cramps, diarrhoea, fatigue, double vision, and muscle weakness.

Vitamin K

Vitamin K is a group of structurally similar fat-soluble vitamins, that the human body needs for blood clotting and bone metabolism. Vitamin K_1 is present in food and its best sources include green leafy vegetables and seaweed. Vitamin K_2 is produced in the body by intestinal bacteria. Vitamin K deficiency is rare unless the intestine has been damaged causing malabsorption, or when the body's intestinal bacterial flora has been imbalanced (e.g. as a result of taking broad spectrum antibiotics). This can normally be corrected with the use of probiotics.

B vitamins

B vitamins are a group of eight water-soluble vitamins that play many important roles in the body. B vitamins are involved in: energy production, nerve function, cell growth, production of red blood cells, skin health, as well as metabolism of fat, carbohydrate, protein, and alcohol. Some of the signs of deficiencies include: emotional disturbances, weakness, fatigue, anaemia, dermatitis, irregular heartbeat, oedema, cracked lips, high sensitivity to sunlight, mental confusion, depression, high blood pressure, peripheral neuropathy, and memory loss.

There are many good dietary sources of B vitamins in a wheat, gluten, and dairy-free diet. For example, gluten-free whole grains, such as quinoa, buckwheat and amaranth. It is worth noting that refined flours (e.g. white rice flour) have low levels of B vitamins. Moreover, the body needs to use B vitamins to process refined carbohydrates. This is why there are many products on the market that have been enriched with B vitamins, e.g. breakfast cereals. Other good sources of B vitamins include: legumes, green leafy vegetables, potatoes, meat and fish (e.g. turkey, liver, tuna, mackerel), eggs, nuts, seeds, and some fruit (e.g. bananas, oranges). Certain groups of people require higher intakes of B vitamins, including pregnant women, elderly people, athletes, people exposed to environmental pollution or chronic stress, as well as people with certain underlying conditions, e.g. fibromyalgia.

It should be noted that vitamin B_{12} can be obtained only from animal foods (meat, seafood, eggs), which makes vitamin B_{12} deficiency a real problem for vegans. This can however be resolved with supplementation. Caution is advised when taking vitamin B supplements. This is because even though they are water-soluble, and in most cases their excess can be removed from the body, some of them can produce toxic effects when large amounts are ingested. For example, chronic high intakes of vitamin B_1 and B_3 (more than 3 g per day), as well as B_6 (more than 1 g per day), have been associated with a variety of neurological problems and compromised liver function. High intakes of vitamin B_9 (folic acid) can mask vitamin B_{12} deficiency, which can also lead to neurological damage. It is however very unlikely for intakes of this magnitude to be achieved through diet alone.

Vitamin C

Vitamin C (ascorbic acid) is essential for the structure and maintenance of blood vessels, cartilage, muscle and bone. It is important for immune function, wound healing, iron absorption and detoxification processes. Vitamin C is a natural antihistamine. It is also a powerful antioxidant and helps protect cells from oxidative stress. This is the reason why ascorbic acid is widely used as a food additive: to prevent oxidation. Vitamin C deficiency can result in scurvy. The vitamin C requirements are higher in smokers, during pregnancy and lactation, for postoperative patients, and in people suffering from chronic illness, or those exposed to stress or pollution.

The best sources of vitamin C are: fresh fruit, vegetables, and herbs (particularly: berries, citrus fruits, kiwi fruit, guava, papaya, rose hip, pineapple, cantaloupe melon, peppers, broccoli, Brussels sprouts, cauliflower, kale, parsley). It should be noted that vitamin C tends to degrade when exposed to heat, light or air, so losses can occur during food storage, preparation and cooking. High intakes of vitamin C obtained through supplementation (more than 1 g per day) may produce diarrhoea in some individuals. Additionally, prolonged high intakes of vitamin C have been observed to increase the rate of vitamin C turnover in the body as the body adapts to the level of intake. If this happens sudden cessation of supplementation can result in rebound scurvy. This provides an argument for intermittent use of high doses of vitamin C (few weeks at a time) and gradual diminishing of the level of intake.

Calcium

Calcium is an important mineral needed to create and maintain our bones. 99% of the body's calcium is deposited in our bones and teeth. The remaining 1% is found within tissues and body fluids, where it influences hormonal secretion, muscle contraction, nerve transmission, and blood clotting. Levels of calcium in the blood are very tightly regulated and do not fluctuate with changes in dietary intakes. The body uses bone tissue as source of calcium, to maintain constant concentrations of calcium in blood, muscle, and intercellular fluids.

Lack of calcium can result in a poor blood clotting ability, stunted growth, and inability to achieve peak bone density in early adulthood, which may compromise bone density later in life. As mentioned previously, calcium is just one of many factors affecting bone health, nonetheless it is important to ensure adequate intake. Dairy is a well-known source of dietary calcium, but for those who avoid dairy there are still ways to satisfy their daily calcium requirements. Good non-dairy sources of dietary calcium include: fish containing soft bones (e.g. pilchards, sardines), seaweed, green leafy vegetables, nuts, seeds, legumes, and some gluten-free grains (quinoa, amaranth, teff). Additionally, some brands of gluten-free breakfast cereals, and some alternatives to dairy products (e.g. rice milk), are fortified with calcium. Whilst it is true that calcium from plant-sources is absorbed less readily than from dairy products, it is important to remember that the rate of absorption can be improved by ensuring adequate intake of vitamin D and magnesium. On the other hand, bioavailability may be affected negatively by phytates and oxalates (e.g. in spinach, rhubarb, chard), as they inhibit calcium absorption, as well as by high supplemental intake of zinc.

Even high intakes of calcium (2 g per day) do not seem to have toxic effects. However, regular high intakes of calcium tend to reduce zinc absorption, and therefore can have negative impact on health. Excessive calcium supplementation can be also detrimental to kidney function and cardiovascular health.

Phosphorus

Phosphorus is a mineral that is present in all body's cells and is closely linked to calcium and protein metabolism. The majority of phosphorus is deposited in bones and teeth, formation and maintenance of which is the main function of phosphorus. Phosphorus also plays an important role in energy production, utilisation of carbohydrates and fats, and in the synthesis of protein for tissue growth.

36

Furthermore, phosphorus is important for nerve conduction, kidney function, heart rate, and acid-alkaline balance regulation.

Phosphorus is present in most foods. Because phosphorus is so readily available in the food supply, typical intakes tend to exceed the recommended requirements. Therefore, in most people deficiency is unlikely to occur. However, phosphorus depletion may occur due to large losses of phosphate through urine or stools (e.g. diabetic ketoacidosis, malabsorption, excessive use of diuretics). Excessively high blood levels of phosphorus are rare and tend to occur in people with severe kidney disease, or severe dysfunction of calcium regulation.

Magnesium

Magnesium is another very important mineral, needed for over 300 biochemical reactions in the body. It forms part of many enzymes and plays a vital role in skeletal development, muscular contraction, nerve transmission, energy production, protein synthesis, and detoxification processes. Magnesium also helps regulate blood sugar levels, promotes normal blood pressure, keeps heart rhythm steady, and supports a healthy immune system. This is why low levels of magnesium in the body have been found to contribute to a number of conditions, including: diabetes, chronic fatigue, osteoporosis, fibromyalgia, migraines, and premenstrual syndrome.

Even though a true magnesium deficiency is rare, many people have magnesium intakes below optimal levels. In addition to that certain groups of people have higher requirements for magnesium. This includes people taking diuretics, antibiotics or anti-neoplastic medication (cancer treatment), as well as those drinking large amounts of alcohol, or exposed to high levels of stress. Older adults, people with poorly controlled diabetes, or intestinal damage, also tend to have higher requirements for magnesium.

Some good sources of magnesium include: green leafy vegetables, fish, meat, legumes, nuts, seeds, spices, cocoa, and unrefined grains. Gluten-free grains rich in magnesium include: amaranth, buckwheat, quinoa, teff, wild and brown rice. Intakes of magnesium in excess of 2 g per day are not absorbed from the intestine. Even though surplus magnesium is rapidly excreted by the body, regular high intakes are not recommended as they tend to put strain on the kidneys.

Sodium

Sodium is a mineral that plays a vital role in the regulation of fluid balance and blood pressure. It is needed for muscles and nerves to work properly. When sodium levels in the body drop below normal, hyponatremia can result. This however rarely happens as a result of low sodium intake in the diet. In fact, most people greatly exceed the recommended intake of dietary sodium. Hyponatremia is more likely to occur due to a sudden drop in sodium levels, as a result of factors such as: overhydration, states of severe pain, diarrhoea, vomiting, excessive sweating in extreme heat, or as a result of physical exertion. Symptoms of hyponatremia include: loss of appetite, nausea, vomiting, lethargy, confusion, muscular spasms or cramps, and loss of consciousness. Recognising the symptoms of sodium deficiency is important because when left untreated, the condition can be life-threatening.

On the other hand, chronic high intakes of sodium can lead to high blood pressure, which is a major risk factor for cardiovascular disease. Too much sodium in the diet may also have other harmful health effects, including increased risk of stroke, osteoporosis, stomach cancer, and kidney disease.

Sodium occurs naturally in most foods, but in small amounts. According to the UK Dietary and Nutritional Survey, only about 15% of sodium intake comes from sodium naturally present in food, and only 10% comes from addition of salt to foods. On the other hand, over 75% of sodium comes from consumption of manufactured or processed foods. Sodium is an effective preservative and flavour enhancer, which is why it is added by manufacturers to a wide variety of foods. Some of the most concentrated sources of sodium include: processed meats (e.g. bacon, ham, sausages), cheese, salted butter, smoked fish, tinned products (unless tinned in water only), salted snacks, pickles, sauces, gravy granules, "instant" foods, ready-made meals and sandwiches, stock cubes, bread, and many brands of breakfast cereals. Sodium, similarly to sugar, is added to foods in different forms so when reading labels watch out for: monosodium glutamate, sodium nitrite, sodium saccharin, baking soda (sodium bicarbonate), and sodium benzoate.

As mentioned previously, most people exceed their recommended intake of sodium and should therefore aim to reduce it to 2.3-2.4 g per day (approx. 6 g of salt per day). In the first instance, this should involve cutting down on processed foods. It is also recommended to reduce the amount of salt added to food, and increase intake of fresh, unprocessed foods. People with high blood pressure, or cardiovascular disease, may benefit from reducing their sodium intake even further.

Potassium

Potassium is a mineral that plays a vital role in regulation of acid-alkaline balance in the body. Potassium, similarly to sodium, is also needed for regulation of fluid balance, and for muscles and nerves to work properly. Potassium depletion can lead to vomiting, diarrhoea, muscle weakness, confusion, irregular heartbeat, and respiratory paralysis. However, these symptoms are unlikely to occur due to dietary shortages, but rather as a consequence of abnormal potassium losses due to e.g. use of diuretics. Potassium works closely with sodium so the balance between these two minerals is important. While sodium is mainly present in fluid outside of cells, potassium is predominantly present inside of cells. The balance between potassium and sodium concentrations in the body is tightly regulated, as it is critical to nerve impulse transmission, healthy heart function, and muscle contraction.

The body's requirement for potassium is higher than sodium, because of the daily loss of potassium in the urine and stools. Yet, people in the Western countries typically under-consume potassium and over-consume sodium. Studies are showing that the relative imbalance of sodium and potassium in the Western world is linked to hypertension, heart disease and diabetes.

Potassium is present in most foods. Some of the most concentrated sources include fruits, vegetables, spices, and salt substitutes (e.g. lo-salt). Provided that kidney function is normal it is almost impossible to cause potassium toxicity by dietary means, as any surplus is easily excreted in urine. However, when kidney function is compromised potassium retention in the body can be dangerous.

Iron

Iron is a mineral found in every cell in the body and is essential for production of red blood cells and facilitating transport of oxygen from the lungs to all body's cells. Iron forms part of the oxygen-carrying proteins (haemoglobin in blood and myoglobin in muscle). It also forms a part of many enzymes and plays a role in production of amino acids, hormones, and neurotransmitters. Iron is important for energy production, as well as healthy immune system, skin, hair, and nails. Iron deprivation results in a compromised ability to transport oxygen around the body. This can have many detrimental effects in terms of cardiovascular, respiratory, brain and muscle function, as well as physical and mental development. Prolonged low iron levels can lead to iron deficiency anaemia. Symptoms of anaemia include: extreme fatigue, muscle weakness, breathlessness, pale skin, headaches, dizziness, inflamed tongue, and fast heartbeat. It should be noted that symptoms of anaemia can also occur as a result of copper, vitamin B_9, B_{12}, or vitamin C deficiency.

Iron deficiency is the most common nutritional deficiency in the world. Groups that tend to be more at risk include: infants and toddlers, menstruating women with low dietary intake of iron, women who become pregnant with low iron stores, and those on poorly-balanced vegetarian diets. For this reason, iron requirements vary depending on age, gender and dietary restrictions. It is important not to self-diagnose iron deficiency anaemia. Even though the body can regulate iron absorption, excess iron as a result of supplementation can cause toxicity, and create other micronutrient imbalances and deficiencies.

Zinc

Zinc is another mineral with a wide range of functions in the body, as it is a component of more than 70 different enzymes. Zinc is important for production of certain hormones (e.g. insulin, growth hormone, testosterone) and it also participates in carbohydrate, fat and protein synthesis, and degradation. Low levels of zinc can lead to wasting of body tissues, as well as impaired immune, reproductive, cognitive and motor function. Insufficient zinc intake can also contribute to: poor wound healing and poor skin health (e.g. acne), compromised sense of taste and smell, decreased appetite, and potentially anorexia. Blood zinc levels have been found to be dependent upon vitamins A and D. Therefore, adequate vitamin A and D intake is required to ensure good zinc status.

Similarly to iron, bioavailability of zinc is higher from animal foods (red meat, seafood, poultry and eggs). This is because phytates present in plant foods inhibit zinc absorption. This is a consideration for people on vegetarian diets. Plant sources of zinc include: cereal products, green leafy vegetables, beans and pulses, cocoa beans, nuts and seeds. Gluten-free grains that are naturally high in zinc include: amaranth, buckwheat, pure oats, quinoa, teff, and wild rice. Supplementing zinc at levels in excess of 2 g per day can cause nausea and vomiting. Additionally, long-term ingestion of high levels of zinc may interfere with absorption of other essential elements, particularly iron, copper and manganese.

Copper

Copper is a trace element (needed in very small amounts) that forms part of certain oxidative enzymes. This makes copper important in fighting free radicals. Copper works with iron to help the body produce red blood cells. It also helps keep the immune system, blood vessels, nerves and bones healthy. Because of its role in facilitating iron uptake, copper deficiency can produce anaemia-like symptoms. Low levels of copper can also result in bone abnormalities, impaired growth, poor resistance to infections, osteoporosis, overactive thyroid, and abnormal glucose and cholesterol metabolism. Most people tend to satisfy their daily copper requirements through dietary sources. Lactating women should aim to slightly increase their copper intake, but this can be also achieved through diet.

Copper is present in most foods. The most concentrated sources of dietary copper include: shellfish, liver and kidney, legumes, nuts and cocoa beans. Absorption of copper can be reduced by large amounts of phytates, as well as high intakes of zinc, iron, calcium and phosphorus. High intakes of copper are toxic and can lead to liver, kidney and brain disorders. However, this has only been reported in unusual circumstances, such as contamination of drinking water.

Chromium

Chromium is a trace element that is needed for carbohydrate, protein and fat metabolism in the body. Chromium stimulates fatty acid and cholesterol synthesis, which is important for many bodily processes, including brain function. Together with some other compounds chromium assists insulin action (Glucose Tolerance Factor). This is why chromium deficiency may be seen as impaired glucose tolerance. Chromium deficiency is often seen in older people with type 2 diabetes, infants with protein-calorie malnutrition, and patients on long-term parenteral (via veins) nutrition. Requirements may be also affected by any nutritional or physiological stress to the body that alters glucose metabolism.

Good dietary sources of chromium include: meat, liver, kidney, seafood, eggs, nuts, legumes, green peppers, spinach, potatoes, corn on the cob, apples, bananas, molasses, some herbs and spices (dried basil and parsley, paprika, black pepper). Gluten-free grains containing chromium include quinoa and teff. Refined foods are low in chromium. Due to the low absorption and high excretion rates, chromium toxicity from food sources is unlikely. However, supplementation with very high doses of 1-2 g per day has been associated with serious kidney and liver problems.

Manganese

Manganese is a trace mineral that is present in the body in very small amounts, predominantly in the liver, kidneys, bones, and pancreas. Many enzymes require manganese as part of their structure. For example, manganese is a component of the antioxidant enzyme called superoxide dismutase (SOD), which is very effective in fighting free radicals. Manganese may therefore have a protective role against ageing, cardiovascular disease and cancer. In addition to that, manganese is needed for formation of connective tissue, bones, blood clotting factors, and sex hormones. It is also important for fat and carbohydrate metabolism, calcium absorption, blood sugar regulation, normal brain and nerve function.

Chronic low levels of manganese in the body can contribute to infertility, bone malformation, weakness, and seizures. Good dietary sources of manganese include: green leafy vegetables, beans, pulses, spices, herbs, cocoa beans, nuts, seeds, and pineapple. Gluten-free grains containing manganese include: buckwheat, pure oats, millet, brown rice and corn. To satisfy the requirements for manganese, it is also recommended to cut down on refined carbohydrates. Even though any surplus of manganese tends to be easily excreted by the body, high levels of manganese supplementation should be avoided as they have been link to neurological disorders. Additionally, excess manganese interferes with the absorption of dietary iron so long-term exposure to excess manganese may result in iron-deficiency anaemia.

Molybdenum

Molybdenum is a trace element that is present in very small amounts in the body. Its precise function and interactions with other chemicals in the body are not very well understood. Molybdenum is thought to be involved in many important biological processes, including: development of the nervous system, waste processing in the kidneys, energy production in cells, and prevention of anaemia and dental cavities. As an antioxidant it may play a role in cancer prevention by protecting cells from free radicals. However, more research is required to confirm the role of molybdenum in the prevention of cancer and other diseases. So far, it has shown promise in animal studies by reducing the harmful effects of certain cancer drugs on the heart and lungs. Molybdenum is used to treat rare inherited metabolic diseases, such as Wilson's disease in which the body cannot process copper.

Food is the major source of molybdenum for most people. Common sources of molybdenum include: beans, pulses, grains, leafy vegetables, liver, seeds and nuts. However, the amount of molybdenum in plants varies according to the amount present in the soil. Humans require very small amounts of molybdenum, and deficiency appears to happen only under extremely rare circumstances e.g. in case of a genetic problem in which the body cannot use molybdenum that is consumed through diet. Similarly, overdoses are extremely rare. Large amounts of molybdenum produce symptoms of copper deficiency in cattle, so it is not unreasonable to expect that taking too much supplemental molybdenum could produce the same symptoms in humans. Those symptoms include: tiredness, dizziness, rashes, low white blood cell counts, and anaemia.

Selenium

Selenium is a trace element needed to help regulate the thyroid hormones and support a healthy immune system. Selenium is also a powerful antioxidant. It plays an important role in preventing free radical cell damage, and therefore may protect the body against ageing, cardiovascular disease and cancer. Additionally, increased selenium intakes reduce the effects of mercury toxicity.

Severe selenium deficiency can cause Keshan disease and Kashin-Beck disease, (predominantly occurring in China), which affect the heart, bones and joints. Suboptimal intakes of selenium have also been associated with compromised fat and carbohydrate metabolism, as well as impaired thyroid and immune system function.

The selenium content of foods can vary widely depending on how much is in the soil on which crops are grown and animals have grazed. In the UK, the selenium level in soil tends to be low. Good sources of selenium include: seafood, meat, poultry, eggs, nuts (Brazil nuts are a particularly rich source), seaweed, and some vegetables (spinach, mushrooms). Gluten-free grains that are good sources of selenium include brown rice and oatmeal. In some countries, it is possible to source selenium-enriched eggs. The body absorbs selenium from plant sources more easily compared to animal sources, but as already mentioned the selenium content in those sources is greatly variable. Selenium interacts with vitamin E, so it is a good idea to ensure adequate intake of vitamin E in order to help boost the body's levels of selenium.

Selenium toxicity is rare but high doses of selenium can be very toxic and can result in a condition termed selenosis. Symptoms of selenosis include: brittle hair and nails, gastrointestinal problems, hair loss, garlic-breath odour, skin rash, fatigue, irritability and mild nerve damage. Brazil nuts contain very high amounts of selenium (68–91 µg per nut) and could cause selenium toxicity if consumed regularly. It is recommended that intake of selenium should not exceed 450 µg per day.

Iodine

Iodine is a trace element that forms an essential part of thyroid hormones. Thyroid hormones regulate metabolism (the rate at which the body uses energy). Iodine also plays an important role in biochemical reactions that affect heart rate, respiratory rate, temperature regulation, protein synthesis and integrity of the connective tissue. In the foetus and newborn, iodine is important for the development of the brain and central nervous system. As iodine is crucial for healthy thyroid function, iodine deficiency can lead to hypothyroidism (underactive thyroid). Symptoms of hypothyroidism include: extreme fatigue, mental fog, goitre, depression, weight gain, and low body temperature. Iodine deficiency is the leading cause of preventable mental retardation in babies and small children. In pregnant women, iodine deficiency is associated with increased rate of stillbirths, spontaneous abortions, perinatal deaths, and congenital abnormalities. Other possible negative health effects of iodine deficiency may include autism, breast and stomach cancer. However, further research is required to substantiate these links.

Suboptimal iodine intakes are still a problem in many parts of the world. Similarly to selenium, the iodine content in foods varies widely due to soil content, irrigation and fertilisers used. It is usually low in areas that are distant from oceans. Seafood, seaweed and sea salt are the richest sources of iodine. Iodine is normally absorbed well but excessive intakes of calcium, magnesium and manganese may impair iodine absorption. It is also true that iodine absorption can be inhibited by goitrogens found in foods such as: Brassica vegetables, millet, soya beans, corn, and sweet potatoes. However, goitrogens are normally deactivated by cooking, so as long as those foods are not eaten raw in large quantities, they should not cause any problems with iodine absorption. The thyroid gland tends to regulate the body's level of iodine effectively, but persistent high intakes of iodine can cause hyperthyroidism (overactive) thyroid, and have been linked to thyroid cancer. Therefore, it is recommended not to exceed 1000 μg per day.

Why is maintaining stable blood sugar so important for weight loss and good health?

As mentioned in the previous section, when we eat, digestible carbohydrates in our food get converted into blood sugar (glucose). Blood sugar is the body's preferential source of energy. Our blood sugar levels affect how hungry and how energetic we feel. They also determine whether we burn fat or store it. The hormone responsible for transporting excess blood sugar after a meal into our cells is insulin (produced by the pancreas). Another pancreatic hormone called glucagon works in an opposite way. Glucagon activates the release of glucose into the bloodstream when the blood sugar level is low. When our diet is balanced, these two hormones work well together, successfully maintaining our blood sugar levels within a fairly narrow range. However, when we regularly consume sugary or refined carbohydrate-rich foods, the delicate hormonal balance becomes disrupted. This is because sugary and refined carbohydrate foods are processed and released into the bloodstream quickly. This tends to cause a substantial increase in blood sugar, which in turn stimulates the pancreas to release a substantial amount of insulin. The release of insulin assists with the removal of excess glucose from the bloodstream. This is an important mechanism, as chronic high blood glucose levels are dangerous and lead to organ damage. Unfortunately for those wanting to lose weight, insulin is a storage hormone. It signals that plenty of energy is readily available in the form of glucose and that the body should stop burning fat and start storing it. As mentioned earlier, glucose is the body's preferential fuel, which means that when glucose is available, the body prefers using it over fat.

To make things even worse, these exaggerated insulin surges can cause too much blood sugar to be transported from the bloodstream into the body's cells. This can result in blood sugar dropping below normal levels, leading to hypoglycaemia (low blood sugar). When this happens, we feel sluggish, irritable and hungry. This is an undesirable state to be in, and because the brain relies on glucose as its only source of fuel, the body responds to protect us. As a result, at this point we tend to crave foods high in sugar. When we eat foods that cause a quick, substantial increase in our blood sugar levels, we feel an initial elevation in energy and mood as our blood sugar rises. This is however quickly followed by a slump in energy levels, and can easily turn into a vicious cycle of temporary "highs", followed by lethargy, sugar cravings, and of course resulting fat storage.

Furthermore, overproduction of insulin, occurring repeatedly over a period of time, may lead to the body's cells starting to ignore insulin (insulin resistance), or the pancreas stopping to produce enough insulin. This can in turn cause excessive build-up of glucose in the bloodstream, leading to the development of type 2 diabetes. Moreover, when the body is unable to effectively use the insulin that is being produced, chronic high insulin levels (hyperinsulinaemia) may result. Hyperinsulinaemia is strongly linked to overweight and obesity, as well as increased risk of heart disease and cancer (in particular colon and breast cancer).

This means that eating foods that "spike" blood sugar quickly and cause repeated exposure to large amounts of insulin is best avoided. This type of eating pattern can result in weight gain (or difficulties losing weight), and other serious health problems (e.g. diabetes, cardiovascular disease, kidney problems). Conclusion: to maintain desirable weight and good health, we need to keep our blood sugar and insulin levels stable. In order to achieve this, we need to be aware of the carbohydrate content of our food, as well as the concept of glycaemic index and glycaemic load.

Understanding glycaemic index and glycaemic load

The glycaemic index, (GI) provides a measure of how quickly blood sugar levels increase after eating a particular type of food. This is important because the effects of different foods on blood sugar levels (glycaemic response) are highly variable. The GI is a ranking of carbohydrate foods on a scale from 0 to 100, according to the extent to which they raise blood sugar levels after eating. This is estimated using pure glucose as a reference, the GI of which has been set at 100. GI values of 55 or less are considered "low," between 56 and 69 are considered "moderate", and above 70 are considered "high." GI values are determined experimentally by feeding human participants a fixed portion of a given food (after an overnight fast), and subsequently measuring their blood glucose response to this food at specific intervals. This process is expensive and time-consuming, and there are only a limited number of laboratories across the world performing these tests. For this reason, GI data is only available for selected foods we consume.

The theory behind the GI is to minimise insulin-related health problems by identifying and avoiding foods that have the greatest impact on blood sugar levels. Before this concept was developed, simple sugars (e.g. table sugar, sweets) had been believed to be digested quickly and cause a rapid increase in blood sugar. On the other hand, "complex carbohydrates" (e.g. bread) had been thought to be processed and released into the bloodstream more slowly. We now know that this is not always the case. While many sweet and sugary foods do have high GI values, some starchy foods (e.g. white bread) have higher GI values than honey or table sugar.

One limitation of the GI is that it does not take into account the amount of carbohydrate actually consumed. This is a problem because the body's glycaemic response is dependent on both the type AND the amount of carbohydrate consumed. This means that you could have a small amount of food with a high GI value (e.g. a couple of jelly beans) and your glycaemic response will be relatively small. Conversely, you could have a large amount of food that has a much lower GI value (e.g. potato chips) and produce a much higher glycaemic response. To correct for that, the concept of glycaemic load (GL) was developed. GL is calculated in a following way:

GL = GI / 100 x net carbohydrate content

(net carbohydrate content is equal to the total carbohydrate content minus dietary fibre)

GL estimates the impact of carbohydrate consumption using GI values while taking into account the amount of carbohydrate consumed. Generally, GL values below 10 are considered "low," between 10 and 19 are considered "moderate", and above 20 are considered "high." For weight loss and general health, it is recommended to choose low to medium-GI and GL foods in order to keep blood sugar and insulin stable. Most experts recommend that the total GL should be 100 or less per day. People with diabetes or metabolic syndrome might want to aim even lower than this. A number of studies have shown that people on high-GI (high-GL) diets are much more likely to develop type 2 diabetes, age-related macular degeneration, cardiovascular and kidney disease, compared to those on low-GI (low-GL) diets. It should be noted that there are times when a quick increase in blood sugar may be desirable. For example, following strenuous physical activity athletes should ingest high-GI foods to optimise their post-exercise recovery. Of course, this is a very different metabolic scenario compared to people wanting to lose weight, or having to control their blood sugar for health reasons. Generally, for people who are physically active and not overweight, daily GL slightly higher than 100 is acceptable.

It is important to remember that glycaemic response varies between individuals and can even vary in the same person from day to day, or from one time of day to another. In addition to that, people can have different insulin responses (i.e. produce different levels of insulin), even with an identical glycaemic response. This means that people who have diabetes cannot rely solely on the GI of foods (or any other food index) without monitoring their own blood sugar response. Moreover, most of the available GI values show the effect of a particular food on glucose levels in the first two hours following ingestion. Some people with diabetes may have elevated blood sugar levels for longer than that.

When using the GI and GL, there are also additional limitations to be aware of. Most of the time GI charts give only one value per food, yet variations are likely to occur depending on variety, ripeness (e.g. unripe vs. ripe banana), cooking methods, processing, and the length of storage. Therefore, you should avoid overcooking pasta, rice, etc. The longer the cooking time, the higher the GI. Moreover, fat, protein and fibre lowers the GI of food. For example, despite being high in sugar, chocolate has a medium GI value due to its high fat content. Similarly, crisps will have a lower GI value than potatoes cooked without fat, e.g. baked potato. This is a reminder that the GI and GL only inform us about the carbohydrate content of foods. The danger of the GI and GL being the only focus in terms of regulating your diet could lead to overconsumption of fat and total calories. This is why each recipe in this book, in addition to the carbohydrate content, provides the fat content information and has a limit of 450 calories (42 recipes are actually no more than 250 calories). It should be emphasised that apart from carbohydrate, fat and calories there are many other factors that should be considered when devising a plan for general health or weight loss. A more balanced approach that takes all those additional factors into account is therefore encouraged (you can read more about that in section *Rules of good health and successful weight management* on p. 48.

The nutritional information provided in this book comes from The Composition of Foods (compiled by the UK Foods Standards Agency and Institute of Food Research), additionally supplemented by the information obtained from the Nutrition Data database (based on USDA's National Nutrient Database for Standard Reference). The GL calculations for each recipe in this book are based on the Estimated Glycaemic Load™ (eGL) obtained from the Nutrition Data database. Nutrition Data used a mathematical formula that allowed a comparison between actual and estimated Glycemic Loads for 221 common carbohydrate-containing foods (Figure 1). Data from *International table of glycemic index and glycemic load values: 2002* (Am J Clin Nutr, 76(1):5-56) was utilised in this analysis. The purpose of this was to produce a reasonable estimate for foods for which GI was previously unknown. Even though those eGL values are only estimates, they enable taking into account foods, which would otherwise have to be ignored due to lack of data.

The GL value for each recipe in this book is a weighted average of the eGL of the individual foods in each recipe. Because cooking affects the GI (and therefore GL) of foods, wherever possible, eGL values of cooked rather than raw ingredients were used for improved accuracy (e.g. in the case of grains or pasta). These values were adjusted for weight changes. Please note that the GL values provided in this book are for guideline purposes only. In order to obtain very accurate GL values, each recipe would have to be submitted for the previously described laboratory tests, which would be both extremely expensive and highly impractical.

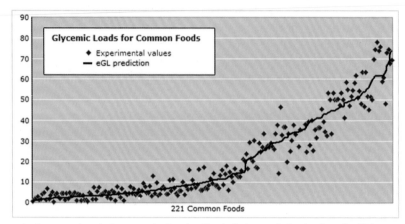

Figure 1: A comparison between actual and estimated glycaemic load values for 221 common carbohydrate-containing foods.
(source: http://nutritiondata.self.com/help/estimated-glycemic-load)

In summary, with all their limitations, the concept of the GI and GL is far from being an exact science. Nonetheless, it is still one of the best tools available in terms of providing information about the impact of carbohydrates on blood sugar levels. This makes it useful when considered alongside other healthy eating tools.

Rules of good health
and successful weight management

Get your carbohydrates right

- Follow an eating programme that consists of low to moderate-GL foods (as described in section *Understanding glycaemic index and glycaemic load* on p. 45). All the recipes and snack ideas in this book fall into this category. This means that if you were to eat a selection of 5 meals and snacks from this book per day, your total estimated GL would work out to be lower than 95, which is the level recommended by many nutrition experts. Please note that if you have diabetes, you should aim for your total daily GL to be even lower, and you should only use the GL in conjunction with other blood sugar monitoring tools.

- Ensure adequate fibre intake, as foods rich in fibre promote stable blood sugar, satiety, and therefore weight loss (refer to section *Dietary fibre* on p. 32).
- Avoid foods and drinks high in sugar and refined carbohydrates. This includes: biscuits, cakes, sweets, white bread and pasta, many processed cereals, canned fruit in syrup, certain sauces and soups (check labels), fat-free products (they tend to contain sugar or artificial sweeteners to replace fat), fruit juices, juice drinks, and soft drinks.
- Avoid adding sugar or flavoured syrups to your drinks.
- Be aware that sugar comes in many forms, so check labels for: sucrose, glucose, dextrose, raw sugar, high-fructose corn syrup, brown sugar, barley malt, beet sugar, buttered syrup, cane sugar, caramel, ethyl maltol, fruit juice, fruit juice concentrate, golden syrup, corn syrup, honey, invert sugar, lactose, malt syrup, maltodextrin, maltose, and molasses. If any of these features as first, second or third ingredient on the list, do not buy it (this is the case with many so-called "healthy" products).

Get your fats right

- Optimise your intake of fats as described in section *Fats* on p 27.

Eat regularly

- Always eat breakfast within 30-60 minutes of waking up and do not skip meals. This way of eating provides you with sustained energy, and ensures metabolic efficiency.
- Eating regularly (every 2-3 hours) prevents your blood sugar from falling below normal levels. As discussed previously, maintaining stable blood sugar levels is one of the most effective ways to promote fat-burning capacity. Three meals per day with small low to medium-GL snacks in-between meals is a recommended pattern. Remember, you do not need a big meal to maintain stable blood sugar. Little and often is the best approach.

Avoid wheat, gluten and dairy

- Avoid or cut down on foods containing wheat, gluten and dairy (to remind you why, revisit sections: *Good reasons to avoid wheat and gluten* on p. 17, and *Good reasons to avoid dairy products* on p. 21).

Ensure adequate fluid intake

- Drink at least 2.5 litres of good quality water every day. You need more when you exercise, in hot or humid weather. You also need more if you are pregnant or breast-feeding, or if you have experienced vomiting, diarrhoea or fever.

- You can count herbal or fruit teas towards your fluid intake, but not caffeine-rich drinks (e.g. coffee). Caffeine has a dehydrating effect and adds to the toxic load in the body. Herbs such as nettle and dandelion support the liver, which is important for weight loss (mixing them with fruit teas makes them more drinkable).
- Fruits and vegetables can contribute as much as 20% to your total fluid intake.
- If your current fluid intake is low, increase it gradually so that your body has a chance to adapt.

Ensure adequate intake of vitamins and minerals

- Whenever possible, prepare your own food using unprocessed ingredients. This puts you in control of the carbohydrate, fat and calorie content of your food, and helps you optimise your intake of vitamins and minerals.
- Eating colourful fruits and vegetables helps you obtain a wide range of important nutrients from your food. Be aware that some nutrients are easily destroyed by light and heat. Store your fruits and vegetables in cool, dark places, and avoid cooking them on high heat, or for long periods of time.
- To assist with weight management, put particular emphasis on eating foods rich in: B vitamins, chromium, magnesium, zinc and manganese (refer to relevant sections on p. 34-41).

Get the balance right

- It is not recommended to eat meat more than 2-3 times per week.
- Aim to eat fish 3 times per week (ideally from unfarmed sources).
- To give your body a break, go vegetarian for at least 1-2 days per week.

Exercise regularly

- Muscular contraction present during physical activity improves insulin sensitivity. Whether it is walking, swimming, cycling, yoga, or gardening, physical activity makes your cells more receptive to insulin. This in turn leads to better control of blood sugar levels.
- Even as little exercise as a 2-km walk every day can drastically reduce the risk of developing type 2 diabetes.
- It is also recommended to do some resistance training every week (whether it is with weights or your own body weight). Lean muscle mass makes the body more metabolically efficient, which in turn makes weight loss and weight maintenance much easier.

- Apart from insulin, physical activity also helps you balance your other hormones (stress, mood, thyroid, hunger, and sex hormones). This is even more important for managing your weight than the sheer increase in energy expenditure. **Remember, successful weight control always has been and always will be a hormone balancing act. There is no getting away from that.**

Spice it up

- Apart from adding flavour to food, most spices and herbs have medicinal properties. For example, cinnamon has been repeatedly shown to play a role in the management of blood sugar levels, as well as other cardiovascular disease risk factors. Coriander may also help regulate blood sugar. In addition to that, coriander has antibacterial properties and contains natural antihistamines. Turmeric has been shown to help fight infections, reduce inflammation, and treat digestive problems. Spices are also rich in essential nutrients.

Steer away from toxins

- Weight management is as much about what you put into your body as it is about what you do not put into your body, so keeping away from toxins is important.
- We are exposed to a wide range of toxins on a daily basis so it is not easy to avoid them, but do your best. These include: pesticides, artificial sweeteners, colourings and flavourings, exhaust fumes, cigarette smoke, over-the-counter drugs, alcohol, caffeine, cleaning products, skin and hair products. Moreover, residues of hormones and antibiotics are found in our water supply and inorganic produce we consume.
- Most toxins have an oestrogenic effect on the body. Build-up of toxins contributes to oestrogen dominance (too much oestrogen in relation to progesterone), which is linked to weigh gain and other health problems (as discussed in section *Good reasons to avoid dairy products* on p. 21.
- Excessive amount of toxic material overloads the liver and other organs. When the liver struggles with excess toxins we feel sluggish and more likely to crave sugary things to give us a temporary lift. This encourages the cycle of temporary highs and crashes. The liver assists with breakdown of oestrogens, so whatever compromises healthy liver function further exacerbates the oestrogen dominance issue. Excessive amount of toxic material in the body also weakens the immune system. Weakened immune system may result in frequent colds and flues, chronic fatigue, or more serious illnesses, such as arthritis or lupus.
- Buying organic produce and natural skin care and cleaning products is one way of reducing the toxic load. Very few people can afford to buy exclusively organic produce so you may want to be selective. Some of the most contaminated foods

include: meat (beef, pork and poultry), celery, spinach, kale, lettuce, tomatoes, cucumbers, potatoes, peppers, courgettes, carrots, strawberries, raspberries, apples, pears, peaches, nectarines, and grapes.

- Some toxins are naturally occurring, e.g. lectins (discussed in section *Good reasons to avoid wheat and gluten* on p. 17). Lectins are present in most foods so it is impossible to eliminate them altogether but there are certain things we can do to prevent overloading our bodies with excessive amounts of lectins. Lectins are fairly heat resistant but vigorous boiling or pressure cooking (particularly when cooking legumes) helps deactivate them. Lectins are also broken down as a result of soaking, sprouting and bacterial fermentation. Plants such as seaweed and aloe vera may also deactivate lectins. Canned beans should be relatively free of lectins but you need to rinse them thoroughly. To further reduce your exposure to lectins: have as much variety in your diet as possible, moderate your intake of grains, legumes, nuts and nightshade vegetables, and avoid eating exclusively raw foods. Some people are more sensitive to lectins then others so you need to gauge your sensitivity level.

- To reduce the toxic load, you should also avoid: caffeine, alcohol, nicotine, foods containing artificial additives, drinking liquids from plastic bottles (especially if they have been exposed to hot weather), and applying perfumed products on your skin. In addition to that, ventilate spaces when using common bleaches and cleaners, and think twice when taking pain killers, or hormonal treatments. To aide elimination of toxins through the skin: use sauna and dry skin brushing, exercise regularly, and shower as soon as you can after exercise, to prevent reabsorbing the toxins that your body expelled with sweat. Finally, maintain a healthy weight, and ensure that you chew your food properly because undigested food can cause toxicity in the body.

Relax

- Modern lifestyles mean that we spend the majority of our days in the stress response. This can have disastrous consequences for our health and most definitely does not help weight loss. High circulating levels of stress hormones (particularly cortisol) have been linked to weight gain, as well as many health problems.

- Spend at least 10 minutes per day doing active relaxation or meditation. You will be pleasantly surprised how so little can benefit your mental and physical health. When you have lower levels of the stress hormones (adrenaline, cortisol) and higher levels of the "feel good", relaxation hormones (endorphins, serotonin, oxytocin), you are less likely to experience cravings for refined carbohydrates. A relaxed state has a positive effect on your blood sugar levels, boosts your immune system, and reduces your blood pressure and the overall risk of heart disease. It also promotes deep and restful sleep.

- Active relaxation involves becoming aware of your body and your physiological reactions so you can switch from the stress response to the relaxation response. There are many active relaxation techniques, e.g. slow, deep breathing (e.g. breathing in for the count of 5 or 10, without straining, followed by breathing out for the count of 10 or 15), progressive relaxation (involves tensing and relaxing each muscle in your body), tai chi or yoga. It should be emphasised that watching TV, listening to the radio, or even reading a book does not count as active relaxation.
- Laugh as much as you can. Watch a funny DVD before going to bed. Laughing reduces the effects of the stress hormones and stimulates the release of the "feel good" hormones.
- Because having the right mindset and attitude toward eating, as well as identifying and changing any unhelpful beliefs about food, is key to successful weight management, I am offering you a free self-hypnosis download (*Achieve Your Ideal Weight*; refer to p. 189 for details).

Get enough sleep

- Aim to get 7-8 hours of sleep per night. It has been repeatedly shown that sleep deprivation has a negative effect on blood sugar and insulin levels. It also raises your cortisol levels, which tends to lead to fatigue and weight gain (or difficulties losing weight).
- Aim for regular sleeping times and ensure your room is fully darkened, as light interferes with the release of melatonin (hormone controlling sleep-wake cycle). Decreased melatonin tends to negatively affect the quality of your sleep. Interestingly, melatonin has been shown to balance excess oestrogen in the body. On the other hand, melatonin depletion is linked with increased levels of IGF-1, which, as mentioned previously, has been linked to ageing and cancer.

Be kind to your thyroid

- Avoid severe calorie restriction (crash diets are very damaging to your thyroid).
- Eat foods rich in iodine, selenium, zinc, iron, vitamins B, A, and C, essential fats and L-tyrosine (e.g. seafood, seaweed, Brazil nuts, chicken, turkey, green leafy vegetables, carrots, radishes, almonds, pumpkin seeds, gluten-free whole grains), and use sea salt for cooking.
- Avoid artificial sweeteners (e.g. aspartame, acesulfame K, saccharin).
- Moderate your intake of foods containing goitrogens, which includes: gluten-containing grains, as well as non-fermented soya products, raw cabbage, broccoli, cauliflower, peaches, pears, strawberries, peanuts, and flax seed. Cooking deactivates most of those compounds but they should not be eaten raw

in large quantities. It is also advised not to juice them.

- Get enough sleep and exercise daily to stimulate your metabolism.

Take care of your digestion

- Clogged-up or inefficient digestive system makes it very difficult to lose weight. Toxic bowel means toxic body. This puts additional strain on the liver and can lead to oestrogen dominance, encouraging weight gain. Moreover, bacterial imbalance in the gut interferes with proper elimination of oestrogen from the body via the digestive tract. People with compromised digestive systems are also more susceptible to nutrient malabsorption, food sensitivities and other health issues.

- Consider taking a good quality broad-spectrum probiotic supplement (this should be stored in the fridge). Be aware that many products found in supermarkets that claim to provide a good boost to your intestinal bacterial flora also contain significant amounts of sugar (i.e. probiotic yoghurts and drinks). Sugar feeds the "bad" bacteria in your gut, which I believe defeats the object.

- As much as possible, avoid stress and the use of medications, such as aspirin, anti-inflammatories and antibiotics.

- You may also want to consider colonic hydrotherapy. However, if you do decide to see a colonic hydrotherapist, do your research to make sure you are in good hands.

Provided, you have no underlying medical condition, implementing these rules will enable you to restore good health, gain your ideal weight and maintain it. Remember, humans are very adaptable and able to get used to most things. Adapting to a new lifestyle is about making informed choices and developing new habits. However, this does not mean being obsessive. As emphasised many times already "moderation" and "variety" are key. If you look hard enough, you can find something wrong with just about any food. So if you become too obsessed with negative effects of foods, you will not be able to eat much at all, or enjoy eating, and that is certainly not the objective here.

You might find some of these points quite easy to implement straight away, while others may take some adjusting to. That is absolutely fine. Make it realistic and sustainable for yourself. Trying to do too much too quickly may not be achievable for you, and it might overwhelm you and put you off. You might find that you are already following some of this advice and that is great. Acknowledge it. Remember, it is not about perfection 100% of the time. Far from it. It is about moving in the right direction, making improvements and praising your own efforts when you are doing well. Many people I work with are in the habit of just placing demands on their bodies and being highly critical of themselves. Let me make it clear. This is a VERY BAD thing. Being hard on yourself when you have had "a bad day" is counterproductive and unnecessary. It breeds negativity and self-loathing, which is not conducive to good health at all. On the contrary, "self-chastising" has a negative effect on your mind, and since your mind and body are connected, it affects your health negatively too. You will occasionally get it wrong. It is human and certainly not the end of the world. Nor a reason to revert to the old bad habits altogether. Put it behind you, move on and get back on track as soon as you can.

Some other things you should know before you start using this book

This book contains 110 recipes divided into seven sections: breakfasts, snacks, soups, salads, light meals, main meals, and desserts. Please treat this as a guideline only. Which recipe you use at which meal is a matter of personal taste. You may find some breakfast ideas work better as snacks, etc. In addition, on p. 179 you find some quick wheat, gluten and dairy-free snack ideas that do not require cooking. Because all the recipes in this book have low to moderate-GL values, having a mixture of five recipes and (or) snacks in one day, enables you to keep your estimated GL below 95.

Please note that the soup serving size is approximately 400 ml so all the soups can be served as meals on their own. If serving as part of a bigger meal, half a portion may be sufficient. Similarly, most of the salads are designed as meals. The salads intended to complement a bigger meal have been labelled as "side salads".

Ingredients

The majority of ingredients used in the recipes in this book can be bought in most supermarkets. This includes many wheat, gluten, and dairy-free ingredients, such as: gluten-free oats, quinoa, buckwheat, gluten-free pasta, gluten-free flour, coconut oil, almond, rice and coconut milk, as well as "speciality" ingredients, such as seaweed and sauerkraut.

A very small number of ingredients used in this book (e.g. stevia, amaranth, sorghum flour) may not be available in your local supermarket. However, those ingredients are readily available online, or from health food shops, and tend to have a reasonably long shelf-life. It should be noted that some of the more specialised grains and flours are not essential for the recipes and you can always use the more readily available alternatives.

Wheat and gluten-free ingredients

As mentioned previously, there are many substitutes for gluten-containing grains (i.e. wheat, rye and barley). Commonly available gluten-free flour blends are usually a mixture of rice, tapioca, potato, buckwheat, and corn flour. You can also buy those flours on their own, but some gluten-free flours take some getting used to in terms of their taste and texture. For example, many people find that white rice flour has a gummy taste to it, which is the reason why I do not use it on its own. I find that flour blends taste more neutral. They work well in most recipes and are better than single flours when used for baking, due to combining different relative flour weights.

Apart from the ones already mentioned, there are many other types of gluten-free flour, including: quinoa, amaranth, almond, hazelnut, coconut, teff, carob, millet, chickpea, soya, sorghum (also known as jowar flour), and gluten-free oat flour. If flour blends available in shops are not to your taste, you can always try mixing your own blend. However, be aware that gluten-free flours have different tastes, and their texture dictates how they behave in a recipe. For example, coconut flour is rich in fibre and may require adding extra liquid to a recipe. Sorghum flour adds sweetness to recipes. Some flours should be approached with caution. This includes legume-based flours, such as soya and chickpea flour. Some people with coeliac disease may not tolerate them well. In addition to that, excessive consumption of soya should be avoided due to high levels of lectins, phyto-oeastrogens, and other undesirable compounds it contains. It is also worth noting that there have been reports of high levels of arsenic in brown rice flour.

Commonly available self-raising flour mixes tend to contain binding components (e.g. xanthan gum and guar gum) and leavening agents (e.g. sodium bicarbonate, monocalcium phosphate). Adding these helps improve texture of gluten-free baked goods. It is gluten that makes regular baked goods fluffy by making dough "stretchy" and helping goods rise. Gluten-free flours do not have the same "stretchy" capacity but adding binding and leavening agents can help improve the quality of gluten-free baking. However, I do not believe that adding gums is essential to every gluten-free recipe. In fact, adding too much of these ingredients can promote heavy, "gummy" texture. It is also worth noting that xanthan gum tends to be derived from corn so may not be suitable for those with corn sensitivity. Guar gum is legume-derived, so those sensitive to legumes (including soya) may react to it. If you need to avoid using gums, try using one tablespoon of arrowroot, potato or tapioca starch mixed with a few tablespoons of warm water. Ground flax seed also works well.

When it comes to baking powder, not all baking powders are gluten-free so ensure that it states "gluten-free" on the label. Baking powder is not the same as baking soda (sodium bicarbonate), even though it contains baking soda. Baking soda needs an acidic ingredient (e.g. vinegar, molasses, honey, maple syrup or lemon juice) to start the gas-releasing process that gives baked goods their rise. If a recipe does not contain an acidic ingredient, baking soda will not work. On the other hand, baking powder will, as it contains both the alkaline and acidic ingredients.

There two types of baking powder: single-acting and double-acting. In order for single-acting baking powder to be effective, the mixture has to go into the oven before the chemical reaction between the acid, baking soda, and liquid ingredient(s) in the recipe stops. This means as soon as the ingredients are combined. In contrast, double-acting baking powders contain a second acid that works more slowly and is activated by heat. This extra leavening power makes double-acting baking powder more effective for gluten-free baking. The amount needed may vary, depending on the recipe. So when buying baking powder, you should ensure that it contains: 1) two acids (e.g. monocalcium phosphate also known as calcium acid phosphate, potassium bitartrate also known as cream of tartar, or disodium phosphate); 2) an alkaline component (sodium bicarbonate or sodium hydrogen carbonate); 3) starch (e.g. corn or potato). You should also make sure that the baking powder you buy is free of aluminium (check the label for sodium aluminium sulphate, or SAS). Two brands worth considering are: Bob's Red Mill and Bakewell. If you find it difficult to source double-acting, gluten-free and aluminium-free baking powder, you can mix gluten and aluminium-free single-acting baking powder with cream of tartar (a third of a teaspoon of cream of tartar for every teaspoon of baking powder). It is worth noting that baking powders start to degrade once the container has been opened due to air moisture triggering a reaction between components.

An example of a flour blend that works well in baked goods is a mixture of equal parts (100 g / 4 oz) of sorghum, oat (or almond) and quinoa flour, combined with 200 g (7 oz) of potato starch (not potato flour), 1 teaspoon of gluten and aluminium-free baking powder, and 1 teaspoon of guar gum (or preferred alternative).

Dairy substitutes

I find that replacing dairy in recipes is a bit more challenging than replacing wheat or gluten. This is particularly true if you want to minimise the use of soya. Soya contains phyto-oeastrogens (mimic human oeastrogens), phytates, lectins, saponins, goitrogens, as well as many contaminants (unless bought organic). The bottom line is that soya is not as good for your health as it was once believed, and therefore I recommend using it sparingly. Consuming excessive amounts of soya may result in malabsorption of vital nutrients, weight gain, digestive, immune and fertility problems. Fermented soya products (e.g. yoghurt, miso, tempeh) are more acceptable as fermentation deactivates many undesirable compounds, but should be still consumed in moderation.

When it comes to substituting milk, there are many alternatives other than soya, including: rice, almond, hazelnut, and coconut milk. I recommend buying the unsweetened versions. All of those milk substitutes can be bought in most supermarkets. Coconut milk is available as "regular" or "light" (lower fat content), and you can also buy it organic. Coconut milk works very well in both sweet and savoury dishes, and is excellent for baking. Some milk substitutes may take some getting used to, but try them a few times, and in different dishes, to give your taste buds an opportunity to adjust to these new flavours. If you are lactose intolerant you may be fine using milk and milk products to which lactase has been added. You may also be able to tolerate small amounts of goat's or sheep's milk.

Substituting cream in recipes is also relatively simple. Non-soya, dairy-free alternatives include rice and coconut cream. Note that soya cream is not always gluten-free so check the label. On the other hand, cheeses are much harder to substitute. Gluten and dairy-free cheese substitutes are usually soya, nut, pea or rice-based. Unfortunately, most of those products do not taste anything like cheese. In fact, many of them taste quite awful and have an unpleasant rubbery texture. Again, if you are lactose intolerant you can probably tolerate small amounts of goat's cheese and lactose-free products to which the enzyme lactase has been added.

Egg replacers

I would encourage you to source a neutral "free-from" egg replacer that you can use in both sweet and savoury dishes. Orgran and Energ-G egg replacers are starch-based (potato and tapioca) and free from wheat, dairy, gluten, egg, yeast and soya. To make your own egg replacer, use 1 tablespoon of tapioca or potato starch mixed with 3 tablespoons of water for each egg in a recipe. The difference in taste when using egg replacers is detectable, but not overwhelming or unpleasant in any way. Using these egg replacers in baked goods tends to make them slightly denser, so you may want to increase leavening to compensate for that, e.g. add additional quarter of a teaspoon of baking powder. If you choose to use egg replacers, it is best to go for flour blends that do not contain tapioca, as too much tapioca will give your baked goods hardness that may not be desirable.

The energy content of egg replacers is much lower than eggs (on average 10 to 20 calories per serving). Egg replacers contain no fat, cholesterol or protein. However, because most egg replacers are starch-based, unlike eggs, they contain carbohydrates. This means that the estimated GL of the recipe will increase (on average by 1.5 per every egg replacer). If you wish to calculate the GL increase per serving in a given recipe, you need to multiply the number of egg replacers by 1.5 and divide by the number of servings.

58

Stevia and other sugar substitutes

Stevia is a plant that is native to South America, where it has been used for hundreds of years. Stevia works well for both, non-baked and baked recipes. The two sweetening components identified in stevia are stevioside and rebaudioside A. They are considered safe when used as sweetening agents in foods and are a better option than artificial sweeteners (e.g. aspartame, acesulfame K, or saccharin).

Recipes in this book do not contain any table sugar. In some recipes honey (which arguably is not much different) is used in combination with stevia. This is because I find that using stevia on its own gives food sweetness that tastes artificial. As usual, I encourage you to exercise moderation. This applies to both, honey and stevia. As long as you have a variety of dishes, and not just the sweet ones, I do not see a problem with using either. Moreover, even though some of the recipes do contain honey, they are designed so that the estimated GL value is kept low or moderate. This means that the total sugar content is still relatively low. It may be worth noting that foods made with stevia do not keep as long, compared to when sugar is used. Therefore, making larger batches may not be recommended.

I would encourage you to source a pure stevia extract, which you can get in the form of drops or powder. There are many products on the market and they tend to vary in potency and taste. The serving size will also vary depending on the brand, and whether it is in liquid or powder form. The recipes in this book specify a number of stevia servings but you may need to adjust that according to personal taste. Please note that stevia-derived products available from supermarkets (e.g. Truvia) are highly processed. Therefore, I do not recommend using them. You may need to experiment with a few before you find the one you like. Brands worth considering include: Sweat Leaf, NOW, Nature's Answer, and Planetary Herbals.

It should be noted that ingestion of larger amounts of stevioside and rebaudioside A found in stevia have been reported to cause bloating and nausea in some people. Furthermore, stevia may have a lowering effect on blood sugar, although the research supporting this is inconclusive. If you have diabetes and wish to use stevia, monitor your blood sugar closely and report your findings to your healthcare provider, as the dose of your diabetes medication might need to be changed. There is also some evidence, though also inconclusive, that stevia may lower blood pressure. This may be a concern in people who have low blood pressure, or are on medication for high blood pressure. Additional considerations when using stevia include: allergy to sunflower and aster plant family (Asteraceae), pregnancy and breast-feeding, and medications containing lithium. Again, check with your healthcare provider if you are unsure if stevia is the right sugar substitute for you. If for whatever reason you do not wish to use stevia, you can replace it with other sweetening agents, but you should bear in mind that some of them (e.g. agave syrup, date sugar, honey, maple syrup, fruit juice concentrate, molasses) do increase blood sugar levels.

Salt

Because adding salt to food is a very individual thing, most of the recipes do not specify the amount of salt that should be added. Instead, I suggest you should taste the food and add the amount that works for you. The exceptions are the recipes containing ingredients which are not recommended to be tasted raw (e.g. eggs). In these recipes the amount of salt has been specified and included in the nutritional analysis. The calculated sodium content is based on using sea salt, which can be changed to a reduced-sodium salt substitute if required. In addition to that, the amount of salt can be changed as desired.

You should also be aware that where tinned products (e.g. beans, sweetcorn) have been used in the recipes, "no added salt or sugar" versions have been selected. Additionally, low-salt stock cubes have been used rather than regular stock cubes. This is reflected in the sodium content of those recipes. Using more herbs and spices enhances flavour of food and compensates for the low-salt options.

Preparation time

Preparation time specified for each recipe is calculated based on preparing fresh produce manually (unless specified otherwise). If you want to further reduce the preparation time, you can use pre-prepared produce (i.e. peeled, cleaned, chopped, or sliced). Or you can prepare larger amounts of items (e.g. vegetables, fruit, fresh herbs, meat) than a recipe requires and freeze the excess for future use.

You can also reduce preparation time by investing in a few simple kitchen gadgets (refer to the next section). And of course, the most obvious time-saving tip: make larger amounts of your favourite dishes and freeze them for those times when you want an extra-quick meal.

Helpful gadgets

If you are a cooking enthusiast, you probably already have some, if not all, of these items. However, if you are only just starting to discover how much fun cooking can be, I would really encourage you to invest in these utensils, as they are both inexpensive and great timesavers. They include: kitchen scales, measuring jug, garlic crusher, electric hand whisk, immersion blender, smoothie maker (or all-in-one blender, grinder and juicer), and electric grinder (ideal for grinding nuts and spices).

BREAKFASTS

ITALIAN MUFFINS

Total Time: 30-35 min; 6 servings (1 serving = 2 muffins)

**115 g (4 oz) self-raising gluten-free flour; 100 g (3.5 oz) gluten-free oats;
2 med eggs (or egg replacers); 300 ml (10 fl oz) unsweetened almond milk;
3 tbs olive or almond oil; 40 g (1.5 oz) sun-dried tomatoes; 100 g (3.5 oz) black
pitted olives; 2 tbs mixed Italian herbs; 0.25 tsp sea salt;
pinch of pepper; sunflower oil spray**

1. Soak sun-dried tomatoes in hot water for 5-10 min (unless bought in oil).
2. Combine flour, oats, egg yolks, almond milk, oil, herbs, salt and pepper (stir or whisk).
3. Beat egg whites (soft peaks).
4. Fold egg whites, chopped olives and sun-dried tomatoes into the mix.
5. Coat a non-stick muffin tray with sunflower oil spray (20-24 sprays).
6. Divide mixture evenly (sufficient for 12 muffins).
7. Bake in a pre-heated oven for 20 min (gas mark 6).

One serving contains: *Calories:* **250** *Total Carbohydrate (g):* **29** *Sugar (g):* **2**
Carbohydrate Portions: **3** *Protein (g):* **7** *Total Fat (g):* **12** *Saturated Fat (g):* **2**
Unsaturated Fat (g): **9** *Cholesterol (mg):* **76** *Fibre (g):* **4** *Sodium (mg):* **534** *Salt (g):* **1.3**
Calcium (mg): **120** *Magnesium (mg):* **51** *Iron (mg):* **3** *Zinc (mg):* **1** *Glycaemic Load:* **18**

BANANA & COCONUT AMARANTH
Total Time: 30 min; 4 servings

**80 g (3 oz) amaranth (can use quinoa or teff); 3 ripe med bananas;
30 g (1 oz) dried cranberries; 100 g (3.5 oz) unsweetened desiccated coconut;
150 ml (5 fl oz) coconut milk; 200 ml (6.5 fl oz) unsweetened almond milk**

1. Cook amaranth as per instructions on the packaging.
2. Drain the cooked amaranth and add mashed banana, desiccated coconut, cranberries, almond, and coconut milk.
3. Cook on medium heat for 4-5 min, stirring frequently.
4. Divide into 4 servings.
5. Serve warm.

One serving contains: *Calories:* **398** *Total Carbohydrate (g):* **34** *Sugar (g):* **17**
Carbohydrate Portions: **4** *Protein (g):* **6** *Total Fat (g):* **25** *Saturated Fat (g):* **20**
Unsaturated Fat (g): **2** *Cholesterol (mg):* **0** *Fibre (g):* **8** *Sodium (mg):* **21** *Salt (g):* **0.05**
Calcium (mg): **110** *Magnesium (mg):* **106** *Iron (mg):* **3.5** *Zinc (mg):* **1.5** *Glycaemic Load:* **16**

APPLE PANCAKES

Total Time: 30-35 min; 4 servings (1 serving = 2 pancakes)

---

70 g (2.5 oz) quinoa flakes (can use rice flakes, buckwheat flakes, or mixture); 6 med apples; 200 g (7 oz) plain soya yoghurt (can use rice cream or coconut milk); 2 med eggs (or egg replacers); 1 tbs runny honey; 1 tsp guar gum (or preferred alternative); 8 servings stevia; sunflower oil spray

1. Combine grated apples with flakes, eggs, yoghurt, honey, gum and stevia, and stir until the mixture thickens.
2. Coat frying pan with sunflower oil spray (6-8 sprays each time).
3. Using a ladle, or a tablespoon, apply mixture onto the frying pan. If you use a 20-cm frying pan or greater, you will be able to fit in 4 pancakes at a time (the mixture is sufficient for 8 pancakes in total).
4. Pan-fry for 3-4 min on each side on very low heat (or until golden brown).
5. Serve warm.

One serving contains: *Calories:* **236** *Total Carbohydrate (g):* **28** *Sugar (g):* **30** *Carbohydrate Portions:* **3.5** *Protein (g):* **8** *Total Fat (g):* **6** *Saturated Fat (g):* **2** *Unsaturated Fat (g):* **3** *Cholesterol (mg):* **113** *Fibre (g):* **5** *Sodium (mg):* **94** *Salt (g):* **0.2** *Calcium (mg):* **95** *Magnesium (mg):* **36** *Iron (mg):* **2** *Zinc (mg):* **1** *Glycaemic Load:* **18**

SUPERFOOD SMOOTHIE
Total Time: 15 min; 4 servings

---

400 g (14 oz) black forest fruit (frozen); 2 med apples; 0.5 large pomegranate; 4 med kiwi fruits; 1 med lemon (juiced); 50 g (2 oz) gluten-free oats; 50 g (2 oz) ready-to-eat prunes (approx. 10 small or 5 big prunes); 25 g (1 oz) chia seeds; 50 ml (1.5 fl oz) orange juice

1. You may want to soak the oats and chia seeds (for a few hours or overnight), and also allow the frozen fruit to thaw first, but this is not absolutely necessary.
2. Cut apples and kiwi fruits into chunks, and blend with forest fruit, seeds, prunes, oats, lemon, and orange juice until smooth.
3. Divide into 4 servings.

One serving contains: *Calories:* **206** *Total Carbohydrate (g):* **41** *Sugar (g):* **25** *Carbohydrate Portions:* **3.5** *Protein (g):* **4** *Total Fat (g):* **4** *Saturated Fat (g):* **0** *Unsaturated Fat (g):* **3** *Cholesterol (mg):* **0** *Fibre (g):* **11** *Sodium (mg):* **9** *Salt (g):* **0.02** *Calcium (mg):* **114** *Magnesium (mg):* **60** *Iron (mg):* **2** *Zinc (mg):* **1** *Glycaemic Load:* **16**

POLENTA WITH EGG & AVOCADO SALSA

Total Time: 1 hr (or 20 min if polenta prepared in advance); 4 servings

---

Polenta: **120 g (4.5 oz) fine cornmeal; 1 low-salt vegetable stock cube; 700 ml (24 fl oz) water**
Scrambled egg: **6 med eggs; 1 large onion; 100 ml (3.5 fl oz) unsweetened rice milk; 0.5 tbs coconut oil; salt and pepper (to taste)**
Avocado salsa: **2 small avocados; 0.5 lime (juiced); 1 tbs olive oil; 2 tbs dried tarragon (or 3 tbs fresh)**

1. Mix cornmeal with stock cube and water (boiled), and cook covered on low heat for 25 min, stirring occasionally. Then remove the lid and cook for a further few minutes stirring continuously, allowing the mixture to thicken.
2. Allow to cool, refrigerate for 30 min and cut into desired shapes (can be prepared the night before).
3. Sauté chopped onion in coconut oil for 4-5 min on medium heat.
4. Whisk eggs with milk, add sautéed onion, salt and pepper, and cook until set.
5. For salsa, mix diced avocado, lime juice, olive oil, and finely chopped tarragon.

One serving contains: *Calories:* **393** *Total Carbohydrate (g):* **35** *Sugar (g):* **3**
Carbohydrate Portions: **3** *Protein (g):* **15** *Total Fat (g):* **24** *Saturated Fat (g):* **9**
Unsaturated Fat (g): **11** *Cholesterol (mg):* **340** *Fibre (g):* **7** *Sodium (mg):* **140** *Salt (g):* **0.3**
Calcium (mg): **90** *Magnesium (mg):* **65** *Iron (mg):* **3** *Zinc (mg):* **2** *Glycaemic Load:* **18**

BANANA & CINNAMON MUFFINS

Total Time: 30 min; 6 servings (1 serving = 2 muffins)

---

120 g (4.5 oz) self-raising gluten-free flour; 50 g (2 oz) gluten-free oats; 2 med eggs (or egg replacers); 2 ripe med bananas; 1 tbs runny honey; 250 ml (8.5 fl oz) unsweetened almond milk (or rice milk); 5 tsp cinnamon; 24 servings stevia; sunflower oil spray

1. Combine flour, oats, egg yolks, almond milk, honey, cinnamon, oil, and stevia (stir or whisk).
2. Beat egg whites (soft peaks).
3. Gently fold egg whites and chopped bananas into the mixture.
4. Coat a non-stick muffin tray with sunflower oil spray (20-24 sprays).
5. Divide mixture evenly (sufficient for 12 muffins).
6. Bake in a pre-heated oven for 20 min (gas mark 6), or until golden brown.

One serving contains: *Calories:* **189** *Total Carbohydrate (g):* **34** *Sugar (g):* **7** *Carbohydrate Portions:* **3.5** *Protein (g):* **5** *Total Fat (g):* **4** *Saturated Fat (g):* **1** *Unsaturated Fat (g):* **2** *Cholesterol (mg):* **76** *Fibre (g):* **4** *Sodium (mg):* **30** *Salt (g):* **0.08** *Calcium (mg):* **94** *Magnesium (mg):* **41** *Iron (mg):* **1** *Zinc (mg):* **1** *Glycaemic Load:* **19**

AUBERGINE CUTLETS WITH HUMMUS

Total Time: 40 min; 4 servings (1 serving = 3 cutlets)

Cutlets: **2 med aubergines; 2 small eggs; 100 g (3.5 oz) gluten-free breadcrumbs; 2 tbs mild paprika; sunflower oil spray; salt and pepper (to taste)**
Hummus: **240 g (8.5 oz) chickpeas tinned in water (rinsed and drained); 1 clove garlic (peeled); 1 tbs tahini; 1 tbs onion granules; 2 tbs olive oil; 0.5 lemon (juiced); 0.5 tsp sea salt; cayenne pepper (to taste)**

1. Slice aubergines into 12 slices, sprinkle with salt and pepper, and bake covered with foil for 15 min in a pre-heated oven (gas mark 7).
2. Coat the aubergine slices in egg (lightly whisked), and then in breadcrumbs mixed with paprika.
3. Pan-fry the aubergine slices in a large frying pan (coated with 6-8 sprays each time) for 2-3 min on each side, on very low heat, or until starting to brown.
4. For the hummus, blend all the ingredients until smooth.

One serving contains: *Calories:* **305** *Total Carbohydrate (g):* **33** *Sugar (g):* **6** *Carbohydrate Portions:* **3** *Protein (g):* **13** *Total Fat (g):* **14** *Saturated Fat (g):* **2** *Unsaturated Fat (g):* **10** *Cholesterol (mg):* **98** *Fibre (g):* **8** *Sodium (mg):* **514** *Salt (g):* **1.3** *Calcium (mg):* **130** *Magnesium (mg):* **62** *Iron (mg):* **4.5** *Zinc (mg):* **2** *Glycaemic Load:* **16**

PINEAPPLE & GINGER MOUSSE

Total Time: 20-25 min; 4 servings

**550 g (20 oz) fresh pineapple (can use tinned in juice); 2 med apples;
2 med oranges; 100 g dried soft dates (approx. 20 dates);
25 g (1 oz) peeled fresh ginger; 0.5 lemon (juiced);
40 g (1.5 oz) ground flax seed**

1. Cut fruit into chunks.
2. Blend the fruit with crushed ginger, flax seed and lemon juice until smooth.
3. Divide into 4 servings.
4. Decorate with chopped dates.

One serving contains: *Calories:* **237** *Total Carbohydrate (g):* **50** *Sugar (g):* **40**
Carbohydrate Portions: **4.5** *Protein (g):* **5** *Total Fat (g):* **5** *Saturated Fat (g):* **0**
Unsaturated Fat (g): **5** *Cholesterol (mg):* **0** *Fibre (g):* **7** *Sodium (mg):* **10** *Salt (g):* **0.03**
Calcium (mg): **78** *Magnesium (mg):* **76** *Iron (mg):* **1** *Zinc (mg):* **1** *Glycaemic Load:* **17**

BUCKWHEAT PANCAKES WITH VEGGIE PATÉ

Total Time: 40 min; 4 servings (1 serving = large pancakes)

Pancakes: 100 g (3.5 oz) buckwheat; 3 med eggs; 80 g (3 oz) chickpeas tinned in water (rinsed and drained); 3 tbs gluten-free flour; 150 ml (5 fl oz) unsweetened almond milk; 4 tbs apple cider vinegar; 1 tsp sea salt; sunflower oil spray
Paté: 3 small avocados; 2 med eggs; 1 small pepper; 3 spring onions; 3 tsp dried coriander; 15 g (0.5 oz) fresh coriander; 0.5 lemon (juiced); salt and pepper (to taste)

1. Cook buckwheat as per instructions on the packaging.
2. Combine cooked buckwheat, eggs, flour, mashed chickpeas, almond milk, vinegar, and salt thoroughly.
3. Apply mixture onto a frying pan (coated with 4 sprays each time) and pan-fry for 4 min on each side on very low heat, or until golden brown. You can use 2 frying pans at the same time to speed up the process (the mixture is sufficient for 4 large pancakes).
4. For the paté, combine diced hard-boiled eggs (boil for 15-20 min) with chopped vegetables, lemon juice, and salt and pepper (to taste).

One serving contains: *Calories:* **370** *Total Carbohydrate (g):* **37** *Sugar (g):* **2** *Carbohydrate Portions:* **3** *Protein (g):* **15** *Total Fat (g):* **20** *Saturated Fat (g):* **11** *Unsaturated Fat (g):* **7** *Cholesterol (mg):* **227** *Fibre (g):* **11** *Sodium (mg):* **95** *Salt (g):* **0.2** *Calcium (mg):* **124** *Magnesium (mg):* **108** *Iron (mg):* **3** *Zinc (mg):* **2** *Glycaemic Load:* **18**

ORANGE & APRICOT PORRIDGE

Total Time: 20 min; 4 servings

**60 g (2 oz) quinoa flakes (can use buckwheat flakes, rice flakes, or mixture);
4 med oranges; 70 g (2.5 oz) dried apricots (approx. 10 apricots);
200 ml (6.5 fl oz) unsweetened almond milk; 2 tsp allspice;
8 servings stevia; 200 ml (6.5 fl oz) water**

1. Bring water and almond milk to the boil, add flakes and simmer for 3-5 min (look for the porridge consistency).
2. Add blended or finely chopped oranges and apricots, allspice and stevia, and continue to cook for another 1-2 min.
3. Divide into 4 servings.
4. Serve warm.

One serving contains: *Calories:* **150** *Total Carbohydrate (g):* **31** *Sugar (g):* **19**
Carbohydrate Portions: **3** *Protein (g):* **5** *Total Fat (g):* **2** *Saturated Fat (g):* **0**
Unsaturated Fat (g): **1** *Cholesterol (mg):* **0** *Fibre (g):* **6** *Sodium (mg):* **12** *Salt (g):* **0.03**
Calcium (mg): **161** *Magnesium (mg):* **48** *Iron (mg):* **1.5** *Zinc (mg):* **1** *Glycaemic Load:* **18**

MUSHROOM & PECAN SLICE

Total Time: 50-55 min; 4 servings (1 serving = 1 piece)

---

80 g (3 oz) cornmeal; 80 g (3 oz) chopped pecan nuts; 300 g (11 oz) fresh mushrooms; 150 ml (5 fl oz) coconut milk (or rice cream); 2 med eggs (or egg replacers); 1 large onion; 4 cloves garlic (peeled); 2 tbs mixed dried herbs; 1 tsp sea salt; 1 tbs coconut oil; pinch of pepper; sunflower oil spray; flour for coating

1. Sauté chopped onion and mushrooms, with crushed (or finely chopped) garlic, oil, herbs, salt and pepper, on medium heat for 5-6 min.
2. Cover and cook for further 5 min.
3. Combine the mixture with cornmeal, nuts, eggs, and coconut milk.
4. Transfer into a non-stick baking tin, coated with oil spray (4-6 sprays) and a dusting of flour.
5. Bake in a pre-heated oven for 30 min (gas mark 6), or until golden brown.
6. Cut into 4 pieces and serve.

One serving contains: *Calories:* **399** *Total Carbohydrate (g):* **27** *Sugar (g):* **6**
Carbohydrate Portions: **2.5** *Protein (g):* **11** *Total Fat (g):* **28** *Saturated Fat (g):* **8**
Unsaturated Fat (g): **18** *Cholesterol (mg):* **113** *Fibre (g):* **6** *Sodium (mg):* **349** *Salt (g):* **0.9**
Calcium (mg): **90** *Magnesium (mg):* **82** *Iron (mg):* **5** *Zinc (mg):* **3** *Glycaemic Load:* **13**

YOGHURT PANCAKES WITH MANGO SALAD

Total Time: 30-35 min; 4 servings (1 serving = 3 pancakes)

Pancakes: **400 g (14 oz) plain soya yoghurt (can use soft tofu); 3 med eggs (or egg replacers); 5 tbs gluten-free flour; 60 ml (2 fl oz) unsweetened almond milk; 1 tbs honey; 1.5 tsp guar gum (or preferred alternative); 8 servings stevia; sunflower oil spray**
Salad: **2 med mangos; 3 med passion fruit; 3 tbs fresh finely chopped mint**

1. Combine yoghurt, eggs, flour, almond milk, honey, gum and stevia, and stir until the mixture thickens.
2. Coat frying pan with sunflower oil spray (6-8 sprays each time).
3. Using a ladle, or a tablespoon, apply mixture onto the frying pan. If you use a 20-cm frying pan or greater, you will be able to fit in 4 pancakes at a time (the mixture is sufficient for 12 pancakes in total).
4. Pan-fry for 2-3 min on each side on very low heat, or until golden brown (wait until well-set before turning).
5. Serve with mango salad (mix diced mango with passion fruit and mint).

One serving contains: *Calories:* **262** *Total Carbohydrate (g):* **36** *Sugar (g):* **23**
Carbohydrate Portions: **3.5** *Protein (g):* **12** *Total Fat (g):* **8** *Saturated Fat (g):* **3**
Unsaturated Fat (g): **4** *Cholesterol (mg):* **170** *Fibre (g):* **6** *Sodium (mg):* **169** *Salt (g):* **0.4**
Calcium (mg): **180** *Magnesium (mg):* **30** *Iron (mg):* **2** *Zinc (mg):* **1** *Glycaemic Load:* **18**

NUTTY QUINOA

Total Time: 25-30 min; 4 servings

---

150 g (5.5 oz) quinoa (can use amaranth or teff); 120 g (4.5 oz) plain soya yoghurt (can use coconut cream); 25 g (1 oz) ground flax seed; 40 g (1.5 oz) ground walnuts; 40 g (1.5 oz) ground macadamia nuts (or Brazil nuts); 500 ml (17 fl oz) unsweetened almond milk; 4 servings stevia (or to taste)

1. Cook quinoa as per instructions on the packaging.
2. Drain the cooked quinoa and add almond milk and yoghurt.
3. Warm up the mixture on low heat for 1-2 min, stirring frequently.
4. Mix in flax seed, nuts and stevia.
5. Divide into 4 servings and serve.

One serving contains: *Calories:* **341** *Total Carbohydrate (g):* **29** *Sugar (g):* **2** *Carbohydrate Portions:* **2.5** *Protein (g):* **10** *Total Fat (g):* **21** *Saturated Fat (g):* **3** *Unsaturated Fat (g):* **17** *Cholesterol (mg):* **0** *Fibre (g):* **8** *Sodium (mg):* **48** *Salt (g):* **0.1** *Calcium (mg):* **248** *Magnesium (mg):* **132** *Iron (mg):* **3** *Zinc (mg):* **2** *Glycaemic Load:* **12**

TOMATO PATTIES WITH SMOKED SALMON

Total Time: 25-30 min; 4 servings (1 serving = 2 patties)

---

130 g (4.5 oz) gluten-free oats; 2 small tomatoes; 3 med eggs (or egg replacers); 80 g (3 oz) tomato concentrate; 160 g (6 oz) smoked salmon; 150 ml (5 fl oz) coconut milk (can use rice cream); 8 tbs plain soya yoghurt (or coconut cream); 100 g (3.5 oz) garden peas (frozen); 40 g (1.5 oz) fresh chives (or 3 tbs dried); 1 tsp guar gum (or preferred alternative); sunflower oil spray; salt and pepper (to taste)

1. Combine oats, chopped tomatoes, tomato concentrate, eggs, coconut milk, peas (cooked as per packaging instructions), 20 g of chopped chives, gum, pinch of salt and pepper, and stir until the mixture thickens.
2. Using a ladle, or a tablespoon, apply mixture onto the frying pan coated with oil spray (use 6-8 sprays each time). If you use a 20-cm frying pan or greater, you will be able to fit in 4 patties at a time (the mixture is sufficient for 8 patties).
3. Pan-fry for 3-4 min on each side on very low heat.
4. Serve with yoghurt, smoked salmon and the rest of chopped chives.

One serving contains: Calories: 400 Total Carbohydrate (g): 33 Sugar (g): 8 Carbohydrate Portions: 3.5 Protein (g): 24 Total Fat (g): 18 Saturated Fat (g): 9 Unsaturated Fat (g): 7 Cholesterol (mg): 197 Fibre (g): 5 Sodium (mg): 893 Salt (g): 2.2 Calcium (mg): 166 Magnesium (mg): 120 Iron (mg): 7 Zinc (mg): 2 Glycaemic Load: 18

COCONUT MANGO FOOL

Total Time: 10-15 min; 4 servings

---

4 med mangos; 80 ml (2.5 fl oz) coconut milk; 1 large pomegranate

1. Peel and chop mango.
2. Blend the chopped mango with coconut milk until smooth.
3. Divide into 4 servings.
4. Serve in wide glasses with pomegranate seeds sprinkled on top.

One serving contains: *Calories:* **207** *Total Carbohydrate (g):* **44** *Sugar (g):* **37**
Carbohydrate Portions: **4** *Protein (g):* **3** *Total Fat (g):* **5** *Saturated Fat (g):* **3**
Unsaturated Fat (g): **1** *Cholesterol (mg):* **0** *Fibre (g):* **6** *Sodium (mg):* **8** *Salt (g):* **0.02**
Calcium (mg): **28** *Magnesium (mg):* **32** *Iron (mg):* **1** *Zinc (mg):* **0** *Glycaemic Load:* **13**

SNACKS

FRUITY SLICE

Total Time: 35-40 min; 10 servings (1 serving = 1 slice)

---

150 g (5.5 oz) gluten-free self-raising flour; 250 g (9 oz) peaches tinned in fruit juice (drained); 2 med oranges; 250 g (9 oz) red seedless grapes; 2 med eggs (or egg replacers); 200 ml (6.5 fl oz) unsweetened rice milk; 3 tbs almond oil; 1 tbs honey; 24 servings stevia

1. Combine diced peaches and oranges with halved grapes, flour, rice milk, oil, honey, stevia, and egg yolks.
2. Beat egg whites (soft peaks).
3. Gently fold egg whites into the mixture.
4. Coat a non-stick baking tray with sunflower oil spray and a dusting of flour.
5. Transfer the mixture onto the baking tray and bake in a pre-heated oven for 20-25 min (gas mark 6).
6. Cut into 10 slices.

One serving contains: *Calories:* **152** *Total Carbohydrate (g):* **24** *Sugar (g):* **11** *Carbohydrate Portions:* **2.5** *Protein (g):* **3** *Total Fat (g):* **5** *Saturated Fat (g):* **1** *Unsaturated Fat (g):* **4** *Cholesterol (mg):* **46** *Fibre (g):* **2** *Sodium (mg):* **29** *Salt (g):* **0.07** *Calcium (mg):* **32** *Magnesium (mg):* **18** *Iron (mg):* **1** *Zinc (mg):* **0** *Glycaemic Load:* **13**

ONION & SESAME BISCUITS

Total Time: 30-35 min; 10 servings (1 serving = 2 biscuits)

---

100 g (3.5 oz) gluten-free self-raising flour; 50 g (2 oz) cornmeal; 25 g (1 oz) sesame seeds; 3 tbs almond oil (or coconut oil); 2 med eggs (or egg replacers); 2 tbs onion granules; 1 tsp sea salt;

1. Combine flour, cornmeal, oil, onion granules, salt, both egg yolks but only one egg white, and knead the dough for a few minutes.
2. Roll out on a non-stick surface to a thickness of approx. 0.3 cm (use a dusting of flour if needed).
3. Use a knife to help separate the biscuits from the surface after they have been cut out (dough is sufficient for 20 biscuits; approx. 6.5 cm diameter).
4. Place on a non-stick tray, brush with a lightly whisked egg white and sprinkle with sesame seeds.
5. Bake in a pre-heated oven for 15 min (gas mark 6).

One serving contains: *Calories:* **118** *Total Carbohydrate (g):* **13** *Sugar (g):* **0** *Carbohydrate Portions:* **1.5** *Protein (g):* **3** *Total Fat (g):* **6** *Saturated Fat (g):* **1** *Unsaturated Fat (g):* **5** *Cholesterol (mg):* **45** *Fibre (g):* **1** *Sodium (mg):* **253** *Salt (g):* **0.6** *Calcium (mg):* **39** *Magnesium (mg):* **23** *Iron (mg):* **1** *Zinc (mg):* **0.5** *Glycaemic Load:* **9**

MULTISEED BOMBS

Total Time: 30 min; 12 servings (1 serving = 1 bomb)

---

70 g (2.5 oz) chopped dried apricots (approx. 10 apricots); 70 g (2.5 oz) chopped dried dates (approx. 10 dates); 50 g (2 oz) ground almonds (or macadamia nuts); 40 g (1.5 oz) pumpkin seeds; 40 g (1.5 oz) sunflower seeds; 40 g (1.5 oz) sesame seeds; 30 g (1 oz) ground flax seed; 15 g (0.5 oz) poppy seeds; 2 tbs honey; 1 med egg (or egg replacer); 2 tbs gluten-free flour; 8 servings stevia

1. It is recommended to soak seeds and nuts for a few hours, or overnight, but this is not essential to the recipe (do not soak if bought ground).
2. Combine all the ingredients thoroughly.
3. Divide the mixture into 12 equal parts and form into bombs.
4. Place on a non-stick tray and bake in a pre-heated oven for 15-20 min (gas mark 6).
5. Alternatively, spread the mixture onto a baking tray and cut into 12 slices once baked.

One serving contains: *Calories:* **152** *Total Carbohydrate (g):* **14** *Sugar (g):* **9** *Carbohydrate Portions:* **1.5** *Protein (g):* **5** *Total Fat (g):* **10** *Saturated Fat (g):* **1** *Unsaturated Fat (g):* **8** *Cholesterol (mg):* **19** *Fibre (g):* **3** *Sodium (mg):* **11** *Salt (g):* **0.03** *Calcium (mg):* **82** *Magnesium (mg):* **69** *Iron (mg):* **2** *Zinc (mg):* **1** *Glycaemic Load:* **7**

SPICED FRUIT KEBABS

Total Time: 35-40 min; 4 servings (1 serving = 2 skewers)

**1 med apple; 1 small orange; 2 large pineapple slices; 16 prunes;
4 small dried figs; 8 dried apricots; 1 tbs honey; 2 tsp cinnamon;
2 tsp allspice; 3 tbs water; 8 skewers**

1. Cut pineapple, orange and apple into chunks (approx. 16 chunks of each fruit), and halve the figs.
2. Put fruit on 8 skewers aiming to have 4 pieces of dried fruit and 6 pieces of fresh fruit on each one.
3. Mix honey with spices and water (if too thick, add more water).
4. Brush the kebabs with the honey and spice glaze.
5. Place on a non-stick baking tray and bake in a pre-heated oven for 20 min, (covered with foil), then uncover and bake for further 5 min (gas mark 6).

One serving contains: *Calories:* **152** *Total Carbohydrate (g):* **38** *Sugar (g):* **33**
Carbohydrate Portions: **3.5** *Protein (g):* **3** *Total Fat (g):* **0** *Saturated Fat (g):* **0**
Unsaturated Fat (g): **0** *Cholesterol (mg):* **0** *Fibre (g):* **6** *Sodium (mg):* **17** *Salt (g):* **0.04**
Calcium (mg): **102** *Magnesium (mg):* **35** *Iron (mg):* **2** *Zinc (mg):* **0** *Glycaemic Load:* **19**

ALMOND & POPPY BISCUITS

Total Time: 30-35 min; 10 servings (1 serving = 2 biscuits)

---

200 g (7 oz) ground almonds; 70 g (2.5 oz) gluten-free self-raising flour; 30 g (1 oz) sorghum flour (or gluten-free self-raising flour); 1.5 tbs poppy seeds; 4 tbs almond oil; 1 med egg (or egg replacer); 2 tbs honey; 20 servings stevia

1. Combine all the ingredients and knead the dough for a few minutes.
2. Roll out on a non-stick surface to a thickness of approx. 0.5 cm (use a dusting of flour as the dough tends to be sticky).
3. Use a knife to help separate the biscuits from the surface after they have been cut out (dough is sufficient for 20 biscuits; approx. 6-cm squares).
4. Place on a non-stick tray and bake in a pre-heated oven for 15 min (gas mark 6).

One serving contains: *Calories:* **223** *Total Carbohydrate (g):* **15** *Sugar (g):* **4** *Carbohydrate Portions:* **1.5** *Protein (g):* **6** *Total Fat (g):* **17** *Saturated Fat (g):* **1** *Unsaturated Fat (g):* **14** *Cholesterol (mg):* **23** *Fibre (g):* **4** *Sodium (mg):* **10** *Salt (g):* **0.02** *Calcium (mg):* **82** *Magnesium (mg):* **71** *Iron (mg):* **1** *Zinc (mg):* **1** *Glycaemic Load:* **6**

APRICOT FLAPJACK

Total Time: 30-35 min; 12 servings (1 serving = 1 flapjack)

---

200 g (7 oz) gluten-free oats; 200 g (7 oz) dried apricots; 2 med eggs (or egg replacers); 50 g (2 oz) ground flax seed; 6 tbs almond oil; 250 ml (8.5 fl oz) coconut milk; 2 tbs honey; 16 servings stevia

1. Chop apricots and combine with the other ingredients.
2. Coat a non-stick baking tray with sunflower oil spray and a dusting of flour.
3. Transfer the mixture onto the baking tray (press down and smooth out with a spoon).
4. Bake in a pre-heated oven for 20-25 min (gas mark 6).
5. Cut into 12 flapjacks.

One serving contains: *Calories:* **226** *Total Carbohydrate (g):* **22** *Sugar (g):* **9** *Carbohydrate Portions:* **2** *Protein (g):* **5** *Total Fat (g):* **14** *Saturated Fat (g):* **4** *Unsaturated Fat (g):* **8** *Cholesterol (mg):* **38** *Fibre (g):* **4** *Sodium (mg):* **21** *Salt (g):* **0.05** *Calcium (mg):* **40** *Magnesium (mg):* **56** *Iron (mg):* **2.5** *Zinc (mg):* **0** *Glycaemic Load:* **14**

NUTTY CHOCOLATE SLICE

Total Time: 25-30 min; 12 servings (1 serving = 1 slice)

---

170 g (6 oz) ground cashew nuts (can use almonds); 150 g (5.5 oz) sultanas; 2 med ripe bananas; 70 g (2.5 oz) sunflower seeds; 50 g (2 oz) brown puffed rice; 30 g (1.5 oz) ground flax seed; 6 tbs honey; 4 tbs reduced-fat cocoa powder; 1 med egg (or egg replacer); 24 servings stevia

1. It is recommended to soak seeds and nuts for a few hours, or overnight, but this is not essential to the recipe (do not soak if bought ground).
2. Combine all the ingredients except puffed rice.
3. Mix in puffed rice.
4. Spread the mixture onto a non-stick baking tray (press down and smooth out with a spoon).
5. Bake for 15-20 min in a pre-heated oven (gas mark 6).
6. Cut into 12 slices.

One serving contains: *Calories:* **233** *Total Carbohydrate (g):* **32** *Sugar (g):* **18** *Carbohydrate Portions:* **3.5** *Protein (g):* **6** *Total Fat (g):* **11** *Saturated Fat (g):* **2** *Unsaturated Fat (g):* **8** *Cholesterol (mg):* **19** *Fibre (g):* **3** *Sodium (mg):* **13** *Salt (g):* **0.03** *Calcium (mg):* **31** *Magnesium (mg):* **94** *Iron (mg):* **2** *Zinc (mg):* **1.5** *Glycaemic Load:* **16**

MULTISEED FLATBREADS WITH AVOCADO DIP
Total Time: 30-35 min; 4 servings (1 serving = 2 flatbreads)

Flatbreads: 90 g (3 oz) gluten-free self-raising flour; 30 g (1 oz) gluten-free oats (or cornmeal); 1 med egg (or egg replacer); 3 tbs almond oil; 1 tbs poppy seeds; 1 tbs cumin seeds; 1 tbs flax seed; 0.5 tsp sea salt; 2 tbs water
Dip: 2 small avocados; 0.25 lemon (juiced); 3 tbs coconut milk; 2 tsp dried coriander; 2 tsp cumin; 1 tsp turmeric; seasoning

1. Combine all the ingredients for the flatbreads and knead for a few minutes.
2. Divide into 8 equal parts, form into balls and then flatten in your hands.
3. Place on a non-stick baking tray and bake in a pre-heated oven for 20 min (gas mark 6).
4. Blend the ingredients for the dip into a smooth paste and season to taste.

* Two flatbreads without the dip contain: 242 calories, 25 g of carbohydrate (estimated glycaemic load: 15),14 g of fat and 3 g of fibre .

One serving contains: *Calories:* **355** *Total Carbohydrate (g):* **32** *Sugar (g):* **1** *Carbohydrate Portions:* **3** *Protein (g):* **7** *Total Fat (g):* **24** *Saturated Fat (g):* **9** *Unsaturated Fat (g):* **13** *Cholesterol (mg):* **57** *Fibre (g):* **8** *Sodium (mg):* **329** *Salt (g):* **0.8** *Calcium (mg):* **118** *Magnesium (mg):* **86** *Iron (mg):* **5** *Zinc (mg):* **1.5** *Glycaemic Load:* **17**

OATIE PEANUT BUTTER BALLS

Total Time: 30 min; 14 servings (1 serving = 1 ball)

---

80 g (3 oz) gluten-free oats; 180 g (6.5 oz) peanut butter (no added sugar; can use almond or cashew butter); 40 g (1.5 oz) ground flax seed; 100 ml (3.5 fl oz) coconut milk; 80 g (3 oz) sultanas; 2 tbs honey; 1 med egg (or egg replacer); 16 servings stevia

1. Combine all the ingredients thoroughly.
2. Divide the mixture into 14 equal parts and form into balls.
3. Place on a non-stick tray and bake in a pre-heated oven for 15-20 min (gas mark 6).
4. Alternatively, spread the mixture onto a baking tray and cut into 14 slices once baked.

One serving contains: *Calories:* **157** *Total Carbohydrate (g):* **15** *Sugar (g):* **7** *Carbohydrate Portions:* **1.5** *Protein (g):* **5** *Total Fat (g):* **10** *Saturated Fat (g):* **6** *Unsaturated Fat (g):* **3** *Cholesterol (mg):* **16** *Fibre (g):* **3** *Sodium (mg):* **75** *Salt (g):* **0.2** *Calcium (mg):* **22** *Magnesium (mg):* **41** *Iron (mg):* **1** *Zinc (mg):* **1** *Glycaemic Load:* **6**

CURRY CAKES
Total Time: 35-40 min; 12 servings (1 serving = 1 cake)

---

160 g (5.5 oz) gluten-free oats; 100 g (3.5 oz) unsweetened desiccated coconut; 120 g (4.5 oz) spinach; 150 ml (5 fl oz) coconut milk; 500 ml (17 fl oz) unsweetened almond milk; 2 med eggs (or egg replacers); 4 tsp dried coriander; 4 tsp cumin; 4 tsp ginger powder; 4 tsp allspice; 1.5 tsp sea salt

1. Steam spinach in a pan with approx. 50 ml (2 fl oz) of boiling water on medium heat for 2-3 min (covered).
2. Drain spinach and combine thoroughly with the other ingredients .
3. Divide the mixture into 12 servings using a non-stick muffin tray, coated with sunflower spray (20-24 spray).
4. Bake in a pre-heated oven for 25 min (gas mark 6), or until golden brown.

One serving contains: *Calories:* **163** *Total Carbohydrate (g):* **14** *Sugar (g):* **1** *Carbohydrate Portions:* **1.5** *Protein (g):* **5** *Total Fat (g):* **10** *Saturated Fat (g):* **7** *Unsaturated Fat (g):* **2** *Cholesterol (mg):* **38** *Fibre (g):* **4** *Sodium (mg):* **326** *Salt (g):* **0.8** *Calcium (mg):* **101** *Magnesium (mg):* **52** *Iron (mg):* **2.5** *Zinc (mg):* **1** *Glycaemic Load:* **6**

POPPY SEED PARCELS

Total Time: 50-55 min; 10 servings (1 serving = 2 parcels)

Pastry: **160 (6 oz) plain gluten-free flour; 40 g (1.5 oz) sorghum flour (or plain gluten-free flour); 1 large egg (or egg replacer); 80 ml (2.5 fl oz) coconut milk; 1 tsp guar gum (or preferred alternative); 24 servings stevia**
Filling: **6 tbs poppy seeds; 3 tbs sesame seeds; 2 tbs sunflower seeds; 70 ml (2.5 fl oz) coconut milk; 50 g (2 oz) sultanas or raisins; 1 tbs honey; 20 servings stevia**

1. It is recommended to soak the seeds for at least a few hours beforehand (or overnight), but this is not essential to the recipe.
2. Combine all the filling ingredients (dub seeds dry if they have been soaked).
3. Combine all the pastry ingredients, knead for a few minutes until flexible and roll out thinly on a non-stick surface (use a dusting of flour if needed).
4. Cut out pastry using approx. 8 cm diameter glass (or cutter), apply a tablespoon of filling and seal the edges (moisten edges with water first).
5. Bake on a non-stick tray in a pre-heated oven for 30 min (gas mark 5).

One serving contains: *Calories:* **179** *Total Carbohydrate (g):* **24** *Sugar (g):* **5** *Carbohydrate Portions:* **2.5** *Protein (g):* **4** *Total Fat (g):* **8** *Saturated Fat (g):* **3** *Unsaturated Fat (g):* **4** *Cholesterol (mg):* **27** *Fibre (g):* **3** *Sodium (mg):* **14** *Salt (g):* **0.03** *Calcium (mg):* **117** *Magnesium (mg):* **56** *Iron (mg):* **2** *Zinc (mg):* **1** *Glycaemic Load:* **15**

COCONUT BISCUITS

Total Time: 30 min; 10 servings (1 serving = 2 biscuits)

**150 g (5.5 oz) unsweetened desiccated coconut; 70 g (2.5 oz) gluten-free oats;
50 ml (5 fl oz) coconut milk; 1 med egg (or egg replacer); 3 tbs honey;
3 tbs gluten-free flour; 1 tsp guar gum (or preferred alternative);
12 servings stevia**

1. Combine all the ingredients and knead the dough for a few minutes.
2. Roll out on a non-stick surface to a thickness of approx. 0.5 cm (use a dusting of flour if required).
3. Use a knife to help separate the biscuits from the surface after they have been cut out (dough is sufficient for 20 biscuits; approx. 6.5 cm diameter).
4. Place on a non-stick tray and bake in a pre-heated oven for 15 min (gas mark 6).

One serving contains: *Calories:* **170** *Total Carbohydrate (g):* **15** *Sugar (g):* **6**
Carbohydrate Portions: **1.5** *Protein (g):* **3** *Total Fat (g):* **12** *Saturated Fat (g):* **10**
Unsaturated Fat (g): **1** *Cholesterol (mg):* **23** *Fibre (g):* **3** *Sodium (mg):* **17** *Salt (g):* **0.04**
Calcium (mg): **12** *Magnesium (mg):* **28** *Iron (mg):* **1** *Zinc (mg):* **1** *Glycaemic Load:* **7**

GINGER FLAPJACK

Total Time: 30-35 min; 12 servings (1 serving = 1 flapjack)

**300 g (11 oz) gluten-free oats; 300 g (11 oz) ready-to-eat prunes;
250 ml (8.5 fl oz) unsweetened almond milk (or rice milk); 2 med eggs
(or egg replacers); 5 tbs almond oil; 2 tbs coconut oil; 3 tbs honey;
1 tbs molasses; 6 tsp ground ginger; 4 tsp ground cinnamon;
4 tsp allspice; 36 servings stevia**

1. Melt coconut oil in a pan on low heat.
2. Combine chopped prunes with melted oil and the remaining ingredients in a mixing bowl.
3. Coat a non-stick baking tray with sunflower oil spray and a dusting of flour.
4. Transfer the mixture onto the baking tray (press down and smooth out with a spoon).
5. Bake in a pre-heated oven for 20-25 min (gas mark 6).
6. Cut into 12 flapjacks.

One serving contains: *Calories:* **230** *Total Carbohydrate (g):* **31** *Sugar (g):* **11** *Carbohydrate Portions:* **3** *Protein (g):* **5** *Total Fat (g):* **11** *Saturated Fat (g):* **1** *Unsaturated Fat (g):* **8** *Cholesterol (mg):* **38** *Fibre (g):* **4** *Sodium (mg):* **19** *Salt (g):* **0.05** *Calcium (mg):* **71** *Magnesium (mg):* **49** *Iron (mg):* **2** *Zinc (mg):* **1** *Glycaemic Load:* **17**

GARLIC & SAGE OATCAKES

Total Time: 30-35 min; 10 servings (1 serving = 2 oatcakes)

**200 g (7 oz) gluten-free oats; 8 tbs almond oil (or coconut oil);
2 med eggs (or egg replacers); 3 tbs garlic granules; 4 tbs dried sage;
1 tsp sea salt; 1 tbs water**

1. Combine all the ingredients and knead the dough for a few minutes.
2. Roll out on a non-stick surface to a thickness of approx. 0.3 cm (use a dusting of flour if needed).
3. Use a knife to help separate the oatcakes from the surface after they have been cut out (dough is sufficient for 20 oatcakes; approx. 6-cm squares).
4. Place on a non-stick tray and bake in a pre-heated oven for 15 min (gas mark 6).

One serving contains: *Calories:* **190** *Total Carbohydrate (g):* **16** *Sugar (g):* **1**
Carbohydrate Portions: **1.5** *Protein (g):* **5** *Total Fat (g):* **12** *Saturated Fat (g):* **1**
Unsaturated Fat (g): **10** *Cholesterol (mg):* **45** *Fibre (g):* **3** *Sodium (mg):* **254** *Salt (g):* **0.6**
Calcium (mg): **32** *Magnesium (mg):* **34** *Iron (mg):* **1.5** *Zinc (mg):* **1** *Glycaemic Load:* **9**

CHEESY NIBBLES

Total Time: 25 min; 10 servings (1 serving = 2 nibbles)

---

200 g (7 oz) soya cream cheese; 50 g (2 oz) quinoa flakes (can use rice flakes, buckwheat flakes, or mixture); 70 g (2.5 oz) ground hazelnuts; 30 g (1 oz) chopped hazelnuts; 7 tbs gluten-free flour; 1 med egg (or egg replacer); 2 tbs mild paprika; 2 tbs almond oil; 1 tsp guar gum (or preferred alternative); 0.5 tsp sea salt; pinch of pepper

1. Combine cheese, flakes, ground hazelnuts, flour, egg, oil, gum, salt and pepper.
2. Form the mixture into a thin tube of 1.5-2 cm diameter (see picture on p. 176). Refrigerate briefly before rolling, if the mixture is too soft.
3. Cut into 20 pieces and coat in paprika and chopped nuts.
4. Place on a non-stick baking tray and bake in a pre-heated oven for 10 min (gas mark 6).

* the nibbles do not keep particularly well, as they tend to go chewy, so it is best to avoid making larger batches

One serving contains: *Calories:* **194** *Total Carbohydrate (g):* **13** *Sugar (g):* **1**
Carbohydrate Portions: **1.5** *Protein (g):* **4** *Total Fat (g):* **13** *Saturated Fat (g):* **3**
Unsaturated Fat (g): **10** *Cholesterol (mg):* **23** *Fibre (g):* **2** *Sodium (mg):* **127** *Salt (g):* **0.3**
Calcium (mg): **23** *Magnesium (mg):* **32** *Iron (mg):* **1** *Zinc (mg):* **1** *Glycaemic Load:* **7**

SOUPS

WILD MUSHROOM & PARSLEY SOUP

Total Time: 30-35 min; 4 servings

**200 g (7 oz) chestnut mushrooms; 40 g (1.5 oz) dried wild mushrooms;
1 small onion; 1 small leek; 1 med carrot; 1 small parsnip; 3 cloves garlic (peeled);
70 ml (2.5 fl oz) coconut milk; 1 tbs coconut oil; 1 tbs dried parsley;
25 g (1 oz) fresh parsley; 70 g (2.5 oz) gluten-free pasta; 1 low-salt vegetable
stock cube; 950 ml (32 fl oz) water; salt and pepper (to taste)**

1. Soak dried mushrooms in hot water for 10 min.
2. Sauté chopped onion and leek in coconut oil for 3-4 min on medium heat.
3. Add stock cube, chopped vegetables and water (boiled), and cook for 15 min on medium heat.
4. Add parsley and coconut milk, and blend until smooth.
5. Divide into 4 servings and serve with pasta (cooked as per instructions on the packaging), and salt and pepper (to taste).

* to make a delicious mushroom sauce reduce water to 600ml

One serving contains: *Calories:* **223** *Total Carbohydrate (g):* **36** *Sugar (g):* **5**
Carbohydrate Portions: **3.5** *Protein (g):* **6** *Total Fat (g):* **8** *Saturated Fat (g):* **3**
Unsaturated Fat (g): **4** *Cholesterol (mg):* **0** *Fibre (g):* **6** *Sodium (mg):* **33** *Salt (g):* **0.1**
Calcium (mg): **58** *Magnesium (mg):* **67** *Iron (mg):* **2.5** *Zinc (mg):* **2** *Glycaemic Load:* **17**

ROSEMARY LAMB & ONION SOUP

Total Time: 30 min; 4 servings

---

1 large onion; 1 med sweet potato; 2 small parsnips; 250 g (9 oz) lean lamb; 3 cloves garlic (peeled); 100 g (3.5 oz) plain soya yoghurt; 2 tbs dried rosemary; 1 tbs apple cider vinegar; 1 tbs onion granules; 1.5 tbs coconut oil; 1 low-salt vegetable stock cube; 950 ml (32 fl oz) water; salt and pepper (to taste)

1. Sauté chopped onion in 1 tbs of coconut oil for 3-4 min on medium heat.
2. Add stock cube, water (boiled), diced potato, grated parsnip, crushed garlic, vinegar, rosemary and onion granules, and cook for 15 min on medium heat.
3. Add soya yoghurt once cooked.
4. Heat up the rest of coconut oil in a frying pan, place diced lamb in the pan and cook for 2-3 min on medium heat, turning regularly to prevent burning.
5. Divide soup into 4 servings and serve with lamb.
6. Add salt and pepper (to taste).

One serving contains: *Calories:* **286** *Total Carbohydrate (g):* **29** *Sugar (g):* **8** *Carbohydrate Portions:* **2.5** *Protein (g):* **17** *Total Fat (g):* **12** *Saturated Fat (g):* **3** *Unsaturated Fat (g):* **8** *Cholesterol (mg):* **46** *Fibre (g):* **6** *Sodium (mg):* **116** *Salt (g):* **0.3** *Calcium (mg):* **114** *Magnesium (mg):* **54** *Iron (mg):* **2.5** *Zinc (mg):* **3** *Glycaemic Load:* **11**

CAULIFLOWER & BASIL SOUP

Total Time: 30 min; 4 servings

**1 med cauliflower; 1 small leek; 1 small onion; 1 med carrot;
3 cloves garlic (peeled); 1 tbs coconut oil; 1 low-salt vegetable stock cube;
2 tbs dried basil; 25 (1 oz) g fresh basil; 900 ml (30 fl oz) water;
salt and pepper (to taste)**

1. Sauté chopped leek and onion in coconut oil for 3-4 min on medium heat.
2. Add stock cube, chopped vegetables and water (boiled), and cook for 15 min on medium heat.
3. Add basil and blend until smooth.
4. Divide into 4 servings.
5. Add salt and pepper (to taste).

One serving contains: *Calories:* **129** *Total Carbohydrate (g):* **20** *Sugar (g):* **7**
Carbohydrate Portions: **1.5** *Protein (g):* **6** *Total Fat (g):* **4** *Saturated Fat (g):* **0**
Unsaturated Fat (g): **3** *Cholesterol (mg):* **0** *Fibre (g):* **8** *Sodium (mg):* **81** *Salt (g):* **0.2**
Calcium (mg): **127** *Magnesium (mg):* **55** *Iron (mg):* **2.5** *Zinc (mg):* **1** *Glycaemic Load:* **7**

MINTY BROCCOLI SOUP

Total Time: 25-30 min; 4 servings

**400 g (14 oz) broccoli; 170 g (6 oz) chickpeas tinned in water (drained);
1 med leek; 1 small parsnip; 3 cloves garlic (peeled); 1 tbs coconut oil;
1 low-salt vegetable stock cube; 1 tbs dried mint; 15 g (0.5 oz) fresh mint;
1000 ml (34 fl oz) water; salt and pepper (to taste)**

1. Sauté chopped leek in coconut oil for 3-4 min on medium heat.
2. Add stock cube, chopped vegetables and water (boiled), and cook for 10-15 min on medium heat.
3. Add chickpeas and mint, and blend until smooth.
4. Divide into 4 servings.
5. Add salt and pepper (to taste).

One serving contains: *Calories:* **165** *Total Carbohydrate (g):* **20** *Sugar (g):* **4**
Carbohydrate Portions: **1.5** *Protein (g):* **9** *Total Fat (g):* **6** *Saturated Fat (g):* **1**
Unsaturated Fat (g): **4** *Cholesterol (mg):* **0** *Fibre (g):* **7** *Sodium (mg):* **25** *Salt (g):* **0.06**
Calcium (mg): **129** *Magnesium (mg):* **63** *Iron (mg):* **5** *Zinc (mg):* **1.4** *Glycaemic Load:* **10**

CREAMY SPINACH & SEA VEGETABLE SOUP

Total Time: 30-35 min; 4 servings

---

100 g (3.5 oz) spinach; 1 small leek; 70 g (2.5 oz) brown rice; 3 cloves garlic (peeled); 25 g (1 oz) dried sea vegetables (arame, nori, wakame or other); 200 ml (7 fl oz) coconut milk (or rice cream); 1 tbs coconut oil; 1 low-salt vegetable stock cube; 1100 ml (37 fl oz) water; salt and pepper (to taste)

1. Cook rice as per instructions on the packaging.
2. Soak sea vegetables in cool water for 10-15 min.
3. Sauté chopped leek in coconut oil for 3-4 min on medium heat.
4. Add stock cube, water (boiled), chopped spinach, crushed garlic and sea vegetables, and cook for 10 min on medium heat.
5. Add coconut milk just before the end of cooking, and mix in cooked rice.
6. Divide into 4 servings.
7. Add salt and pepper (to taste).

One serving contains: *Calories:* **216** *Total Carbohydrate (g):* **21** *Sugar (g):* **2** *Carbohydrate Portions:* **2** *Protein (g):* **4** *Total Fat (g):* **13** *Saturated Fat (g):* **7** *Unsaturated Fat (g):* **4** *Cholesterol (mg):* **0** *Fibre (g):* **5** *Sodium (mg):* **35** *Salt (g):* **0.1** *Calcium (mg):* **117** *Magnesium (mg):* **100** *Iron (mg):* **3** *Zinc (mg):* **1** *Glycaemic Load:* **12**

CUCUMBER & DILL CHICKEN SOUP

Total Time: 35-40 min; 4 servings

---

300 g (11 oz) pickled sour cucumber; 0.5 large fresh cucumber; 1 med onion; 1 med carrot; 1 small parsnip; 3 cloves garlic (peeled); 3 small potatoes; 2 small chicken breasts; 100 ml (3.5 fl oz) coconut milk (or rice cream); 2 tbs dried dill; 15 g (0.5 oz) fresh dill; 1.5 tbs coconut oil; 1 low-salt vegetable stock cube; 700 ml (24 fl oz) water; salt and pepper (to taste)

1. Sauté chopped onion in 1 tbs of coconut oil for 3-4 min on medium heat.
2. Add stock cube, water (boiled), crushed garlic, dried dill, and grated cucumber, carrot and parsnip, and cook for 10-15 min on medium heat.
3. Add chopped fresh dill and coconut milk just before the end of cooking.
4. Cook diced potatoes separately (10-15 min on medium heat, or until cooked).
5. Pan-fry diced chicken in 0.5 tbs of coconut oil for 8-10 min on medium heat (check it is cooked through).
6. Add potatoes and chicken to the soup.
7. Divide into 4 servings, and add salt and pepper to taste.

One serving contains: *Calories:* **246** *Total Carbohydrate (g):* **24** *Sugar (g):* **5** *Carbohydrate Portions:* **2** *Protein (g):* **16** *Total Fat (g):* **11** *Saturated Fat (g):* **4** *Unsaturated Fat (g):* **5** *Cholesterol (mg):* **35** *Fibre (g):* **5** *Sodium (mg):* **815** *Salt (g):* **2** *Calcium (mg):* **80** *Magnesium (mg):* **67** *Iron (mg):* **3** *Zinc (mg):* **1** *Glycaemic Load:* **9**

NUTTY TOMATO SOUP

Total Time: 25-30 min; 4 servings

---

2 tins chopped tomatoes; 80 g (3 oz) smooth peanut butter (no added sugar; can use almond or cashew butter); 1 med onion; 1 small parsnip; 1 large carrot; 2 cloves garlic (peeled); 1 tbs coconut oil; 1 low-salt vegetable stock cube; 2 tbs dried coriander; 500 ml (17 fl oz) water; salt and pepper (to taste)

1. Sauté chopped onion in coconut oil for 3-4 min on medium heat.
2. Add stock cube, tomatoes, chopped vegetables, coriander and water (boiled), and cook for 10-15 min on medium heat.
3. Add peanut butter and blend until smooth.
4. Divide into 4 servings.
5. Add salt and pepper (to taste).

* to make a delicious tomato sauce reduce water to 250ml

One serving contains: *Calories:* **236** *Total Carbohydrate (g):* **22** *Sugar (g):* **11** *Carbohydrate Portions:* **2** *Protein (g):* **8** *Total Fat (g):* **15** *Saturated Fat (g):* **8** *Unsaturated Fat (g):* **5** *Cholesterol (mg):* **0** *Fibre (g):* **6** *Sodium (mg):* **201** *Salt (g):* **0.5** *Calcium (mg):* **78** *Magnesium (mg):* **75** *Iron (mg):* **2** *Zinc (mg):* **1** *Glycaemic Load:* **9**

CURRIED MEATBALL SOUP

Total Time: 45 min; 4 servings

Soup: 1 med onions; 1 med carrot; 1 small parsnip; 4 small potatoes;
150 ml (5 fl oz) coconut milk; 30 g (1 oz) fresh coriander; 2 tsp allspice;
2 tsp dried coriander; 2 tsp cumin powder; 2 tsp ginger powder;
1 tsp turmeric; 1 tbs coconut oil; 1 low-salt vegetable stock cube;
800 ml (27 fl oz) water; salt and pepper (to taste)
Meatballs: refer to p. 178 for details

1. To make the soup, sauté chopped onions in coconut oil for 3-4 min on medium heat.
2. Add stock cube, water (boiled), chopped vegetables and spices, and cook for 15 min on medium heat.
3. Once cooked, add coconut milk and chopped coriander .
4. Cook diced potatoes separately (10-15 min on medium heat, or until cooked).
5. Prepare the meatballs following the recipe on p. 178.
6. Serve the soup with meatballs and potatoes, and add salt and pepper to taste.

One serving contains: *Calories:* **347** *Total Carbohydrate (g):* **37** *Sugar (g):* **5**
Carbohydrate Portions: **3.5** *Protein (g):* **17** *Total Fat (g):* **16** *Saturated Fat (g):* **7**
Unsaturated Fat (g): **7** *Cholesterol (mg):* **29** *Fibre (g):* **7** *Sodium (mg):* **659** *Salt (g):* **1.7**
Calcium (mg): **105** *Magnesium (mg):* **89** *Iron (mg):* **6** *Zinc (mg):* **3** *Glycaemic Load:* **16**

BEETROOT SOUP WITH DUMPLINGS

Total Time: 25 min; 4 servings

Soup: 8 med beetroots (cooked in water); 1 large onion; 4 cloves garlic (peeled); 1 tbs coconut oil; 1 low-salt vegetable stock cube; 1 tbs dried marjoram; 1 tbs onion granules; 3 tbs apple cider vinegar; 50 ml (2 fl oz) coconut milk (or rice cream); 700 ml (24 fl oz) water; salt and pepper (to taste)
Dumplings: refer to p. 176 for details

1. Sauté chopped onion in coconut oil for 3-4 min on medium heat.
2. Add stock cube, crushed garlic and chopped (or grated) beetroot, marjoram, onion granules, vinegar, and water (boiled), and cook for 10 min on medium heat.
3. Add coconut milk and blend until smooth.
4. For dumplings, refer to p. 176.
5. Divide into 4 servings.
6. Add salt and pepper (to taste).

One serving contains: *Calories:* **241** *Total Carbohydrate (g):* **38** *Sugar (g):* **15** *Carbohydrate Portions:* **3.5** *Protein (g):* **17** *Total Fat (g):* **8** *Saturated Fat (g):* **2** *Unsaturated Fat (g):* **4** *Cholesterol (mg):* **49** *Fibre (g):* **6** *Sodium (mg):* **289** *Salt (g):* **0.7** *Calcium (mg):* **80** *Magnesium (mg):* **68** *Iron (mg):* **3** *Zinc (mg):* **1** *Glycaemic Load:* **18**

GARDEN PEA & COD SOUP

Total Time: 35-40 min; 4 servings

**350 g (12.5) garden peas (frozen); 0.25 med cabbage; 200 g (7 oz) cod fillet;
1 med leek; 4 spring onions; 25 g (1 oz) fresh chives (or 2 tbs dried);
2 med eggs (optional); 3 cloves garlic (peeled); 1 tbs coconut oil;
1 low-salt vegetable stock cube; 2 tbs coconut milk (optional);
950 ml (32 fl oz) water; salt and pepper (to taste)**

1. Sauté chopped leek in coconut oil for 3-4 min on medium heat.
2. Add stock cube, water (boiled), peas, crushed garlic, chopped cabbage and spring onions, and cook for 20 min on medium heat.
3. Add chives and blend until smooth.
4. Cover cod in water with coconut milk and cook for 3-4 min (or until the cod starts flaking).
5. Serve soup with cooked cod and boiled egg (divide into 4 servings).
6. Add salt and pepper (to taste).

One serving contains: *Calories:* **223** *Total Carbohydrate (g):* **20** *Sugar (g):* **7**
Carbohydrate Portions: **2** *Protein (g):* **18** *Total Fat (g):* **8** *Saturated Fat (g):* **1**
Unsaturated Fat (g): **5** *Cholesterol (mg):* **136** *Fibre (g):* **6** *Sodium (mg):* **161** *Salt (g):* **0.4**
Calcium (mg): **100** *Magnesium (mg):* **56** *Iron (mg):* **3** *Zinc (mg):* **1.5** *Glycaemic Load:* **8**

LEEK & MACADAMIA SOUP

Total Time: 25-30 min; 4 servings

---

1 small leek; 2 med carrots; 80 g (3 oz) ground macadamia nuts (can use almonds); 3 cloves garlic (peeled); 2 tbs flaked almonds; 0.5 med lemon (juiced); 1 low-salt vegetable stock cube; 1 tbs coconut oil; 800 ml water; salt and pepper (to taste)

1. Sauté chopped leeks in coconut oil for 3-4 min on medium heat.
2. Add stock cube, chopped carrots, crushed garlic and water (boiled), and cook for 10-15 min on medium heat.
3. Add macadamia nuts and lemon juice, and blend until smooth.
4. Divide into 4 servings.
5. Decorate with flaked almonds, and add salt and pepper to taste.

One serving contains: *Calories:* **309** *Total Carbohydrate (g):* **26** *Sugar (g):* **8** *Carbohydrate Portions:* **2.5** *Protein (g):* **5** *Total Fat (g):* **22** *Saturated Fat (g):* **3** *Unsaturated Fat (g):* **18** *Cholesterol (mg):* **0** *Fibre (g):* **6** *Sodium (mg):* **52** *Salt (g):* **0.1** *Calcium (mg):* **122** *Magnesium (mg):* **83** *Iron (mg):* **4** *Zinc (mg):* **1** *Glycaemic Load:* **7**

CARROT & TARRAGON SOUP

Total Time: 40 min; 4 servings

---

120 g (4.5 oz) red lentils; 1 small leek; 4 med carrots; 1 med orange; 100 g (3.5 oz) plain soya yoghurt (or rice cream); 2 tbs dried tarragon; 1 tbs coconut oil; 1 low-salt vegetable stock cube; 1000 ml (34 fl oz) water; salt and pepper (to taste)

1. Sauté chopped leek in coconut oil for 3-4 min on medium heat.
2. Add stock cube, water (boiled), lentils (well-rinsed), grated carrots, chopped orange and tarragon, and cook for 25-30 min on medium heat.
3. Add yoghurt once cooked.
4. Divide into 4 servings.
5. Add salt and pepper (to taste).

One serving contains: *Calories:* **223** *Total Carbohydrate (g):* **33** *Sugar (g):* **8** *Carbohydrate Portions:* **3** *Protein (g):* **11** *Total Fat (g):* **6** *Saturated Fat (g):* **1** *Unsaturated Fat (g):* **4** *Cholesterol (mg):* **0** *Fibre (g):* **7** *Sodium (mg):* **87** *Salt (g):* **0.2** *Calcium (mg):* **119** *Magnesium (mg):* **49** *Iron (mg):* **4** *Zinc (mg):* **2** *Glycaemic Load:* **15**

SAUERKRAUT SOUP

Total Time: 35 min; 4 servings

---

220 g (8 oz) sauerkraut; 2 med onions; 1 med carrot; 2 small parsnips; 3 cloves garlic (peeled); 2 small potatoes; 150 g (5.5 oz) lean unsmoked bacon; 5 bay leaves; 1 tbs coconut oil; 1 low-salt vegetable stock cube; 750 ml (25 fl oz) water; salt and pepper (to taste)

1. Sauté chopped onions in coconut oil for 3-4 min on medium heat.
2. Add stock cube, water (boiled), bay leaves, crushed garlic, sauerkraut (rinsed and chopped), grated carrot and parsnip, and cook for 15-20 min on medium heat.
3. Pan-fry chopped bacon on its own (2-3 min on medium heat).
4. Cook diced potatoes separately (10-15 min on medium heat, or until cooked).
5. Add potatoes and bacon to the soup.
6. Divide into 4 servings.
7. Add salt and pepper (to taste).

One serving contains: *Calories:* **185** *Total Carbohydrate (g):* **26** *Sugar (g):* **7** *Carbohydrate Portions:* **2.5** *Protein (g):* **9** *Total Fat (g):* **6** *Saturated Fat (g):* **1** *Unsaturated Fat (g):* **4** *Cholesterol (mg):* **9** *Fibre (g):* **6** *Sodium (mg):* **791** *Salt (g):* **2** *Calcium (mg):* **69** *Magnesium (mg):* **45** *Iron (mg):* **2** *Zinc (mg):* **1** *Glycaemic Load:* **9**

THAI VEGETABLE SOUP

Total Time: 30 min; 4 servings

---

150 g (5.5 oz) mangetout; 150 g (5.5 oz) baby corn; 120 g (4.5 oz) bean sprouts; 6 spring onions; 70 g (2.5 oz) brown rice; 3 cloves garlic (peeled); 250 ml (8.5 fl oz) coconut milk; 1 tbs onion granules; 1 tbs garlic powder; 2 tbs ginger powder; 2-3 tsp dairy-free lemon grass paste; 15 g (0.5 oz) fresh coriander; 2 tbs gluten-free soya sauce; 1 low-salt vegetable stock cube; 800 ml (27 fl oz) water; salt and pepper (to taste)

1. Cook rice as per instructions on the packaging.
2. Put stock cube, chopped vegetables, crushed garlic, spices, soya sauce and water (boiled) in a large sauce pan, and cook for 10 min on medium heat.
3. Add coconut milk and chopped coriander just before the end of cooking, and mix in cooked rice.
4. Divide into 4 servings.
5. Add salt and pepper (to taste).

One serving contains: *Calories:* **261** *Total Carbohydrate (g):* **32** *Sugar (g):* **7**
Carbohydrate Portions: **3** *Protein (g):* **8** *Total Fat (g):* **12** *Saturated Fat (g):* **9**
Unsaturated Fat (g): **2** *Cholesterol (mg):* **0** *Fibre (g):* **5** *Sodium (mg):* **587** *Salt (g):* **1.5**
Calcium (mg): **64** *Magnesium (mg):* **94** *Iron (mg):* **4** *Zinc (mg):* **2** *Glycaemic Load:* **18**

CELERY & WALNUT SOUP

Total Time: 25-30 min; 4 servings

---

400 g (14 oz) celery; 1 small onion; 1 small leek; 1 med carrot; 1 small parsnip; 3 cloves garlic (peeled); 100 g (3.5 oz) walnuts; 1 tbs coconut oil; 1 low-salt vegetable stock cube; 900 ml (30 oz) water; salt and pepper (to taste)

1. Sauté chopped onion and leek in coconut oil for 3-4 min on medium heat.
2. Add stock cube, chopped vegetables and water (boiled), and cook for 10-15 min on medium heat.
3. Add walnuts and blend until smooth.
4. Divide into 4 servings.
5. Add salt and pepper (to taste).

One serving contains: *Calories:* **265** *Total Carbohydrate (g):* **18** *Sugar (g):* **6** *Carbohydrate Portions:* **1.5** *Protein (g):* **6** *Total Fat (g):* **21** *Saturated Fat (g):* **2** *Unsaturated Fat (g):* **17** *Cholesterol (mg):* **0** *Fibre (g):* **6** *Sodium (mg):* **102** *Salt (g):* **0.3** *Calcium (mg):* **104** *Magnesium (mg):* **69** *Iron (mg):* **2** *Zinc (mg):* **1** *Glycaemic Load:* **5**

SALADS

FRUITY TURKEY SALAD

Total Time: 20-25 min; 4 servings

---

300 g (11 oz) turkey breast; 3 med apples; 300 g (11 oz) red seedless grapes; 250 g (9 oz) celery; 100 g (3.5 oz) pecan nuts; 150 g (5.5 oz) kidney beans tinned in water (rinsed and drained); 5 tbs plain soya yoghurt; 2 tbs coconut milk; 0.5 tbs coconut oil; 0.5 lemon (juiced); salt and pepper (to taste)

1. Pan-fry diced turkey breast in coconut oil and lemon juice, with a pinch of salt and pepper, for 6-7 min on medium heat (check it is cooked through).
2. Combine cooked turkey with diced apples, halved grapes, chopped celery and pecan nuts, kidney beans, yoghurt, and coconut milk.
3. Divide into 4 servings
4. Add salt and pepper (to taste).

One serving contains: *Calories:* **445** *Total Carbohydrate (g):* **41** *Sugar (g):* **26** *Carbohydrate Portions:* **3.5** *Protein (g):* **26** *Total Fat (g):* **22** *Saturated Fat (g):* **3** *Unsaturated Fat (g):* **18** *Cholesterol (mg):* **43** *Fibre (g):* **9** *Sodium (mg):* **117** *Salt (g):* **0.3** *Calcium (mg):* **117** *Magnesium (mg):* **82** *Iron (mg):* **2.4** *Zinc (mg):* **2** *Glycaemic Load:* **12**

SARDINE & EGG SALAD

Total Time: 25-30 min; 4 servings

---

4 tins sardines in tomato sauce (95 g each; 3.5 oz); 120 g (4.5 oz) butter beans tinned in water (rinsed and drained); 4 med eggs; 2 med potatoes; 1 large onion; 1 med yellow pepper; 50 g (2 oz) baby spinach; 3 tbs plain soya yoghurt; 25 g (1 oz) fresh parsley; 8 cherry tomatoes; salt and pepper (to taste)

1. Cook diced potatoes for 10-15 min on medium heat, or until cooked.
2. Combine boiled potatoes with chopped onion, pepper, spinach and parsley, crushed sardines, diced hard-boiled eggs (boil for 15-20 min), halved tomatoes, beans and yoghurt.
3. Divide into 4 servings
4. Add salt and pepper (to taste).

One serving contains: *Calories:* **379** *Total Carbohydrate (g):* **29** *Sugar (g):* **8** *Carbohydrate Portions:* **2.5** *Protein (g):* **29** *Total Fat (g):* **17** *Saturated Fat (g):* **5** *Unsaturated Fat (g):* **10** *Cholesterol (mg):* **300** *Fibre (g):* **5** *Sodium (mg):* **451** *Salt (g):* **1.1** *Calcium (mg):* **509** *Magnesium (mg):* **131** *Iron (mg):* **9** *Zinc (mg):* **4** *Glycaemic Load:* **12**

AVOCADO & BEETROOT PASTA SALAD
Total Time: 25 min; 4 servings

---

3 small avocados; 2 med beetroot (cooked in water), 60 g (2 oz) gluten-free pasta;
250 g (9 oz) cucumber; 100 g (3.5 oz) baby spinach; 70 g (2.5 oz) chickpeas
tinned in water (rinsed and drained); 3 med apples; 100 g (3.5 oz) pinto beans
tinned in water (rinsed and drained); 15 g (0.5 oz) fresh coriander; 2 tbs olive oil;
1 tbs balsamic glaze; 1 tbs balsamic vinegar; salt and pepper (to taste)

1. Cook pasta as per instructions on the packaging and rinse with cold water
   once cooked.
2. Mix pasta with diced vegetables, chickpeas, beans, chopped coriander and
   spinach.
3. Mix olive oil, balsamic glaze and balsamic vinegar, and combine with the
   salad.
4. Divide into 4 servings
5. Add salt and pepper (to taste).

One serving contains: *Calories:* **351** *Total Carbohydrate (g):* **45** *Sugar (g):* **15**
Carbohydrate Portions: **4** *Protein (g):* **8** *Total Fat (g):* **18** *Saturated Fat (g):* **10**
Unsaturated Fat (g): **7** *Cholesterol (mg):* **0** *Fibre (g):* **12** *Sodium (mg):* **64** *Salt (g):* **0.2**
Calcium (mg): **80** *Magnesium (mg):* **98** *Iron (mg):* **3** *Zinc (mg):* **2** *Glycaemic Load:* **19**

SAUERKRAUT & CHICKEN SALAD

Total Time: 30-35 min; 4 servings

---

2 chicken breasts (approx. 300 g; 11 oz); 300 g (11 oz) sauerkraut; 2 small sweet potatoes; 80 g (3 oz) garden peas (frozen); 80 g (3 oz) kidney beans tinned in water (rinsed and drained); 1 large onion; 1 large carrot; 1 med green pepper; 3 tbs dried dill; 2 tbs apple cider vinegar; 2 tbs olive oil; 0.5 tbs coconut oil; 1 low-salt vegetable stock cube; salt and pepper (to taste)

1. Cook diced potatoes for 8-10 min on medium heat, or until cooked.
2. Pan-fry diced chicken breast with a crushed stock cube in coconut oil for 8-10 min on medium heat (check it is cooked through).
3. Cook peas as per instructions on the packaging.
4. Combine cooked chicken, potatoes and peas with chopped sauerkraut (rinse first), onion, pepper and dill, beans, grated carrot, olive oil, and vinegar.
5. Divide into 4 servings
6. Add salt and pepper (to taste).

One serving contains: *Calories:* **328** *Total Carbohydrate (g):* **39** *Sugar (g):* **11** *Carbohydrate Portions:* **3.5** *Protein (g):* **25** *Total Fat (g):* **9** *Saturated Fat (g):* **1** *Unsaturated Fat (g):* **7** *Cholesterol (mg):* **53** *Fibre (g):* **10** *Sodium (mg):* **641** *Salt (g):* **1.6** *Calcium (mg):* **137** *Magnesium (mg):* **88** *Iron (mg):* **4** *Zinc (mg):* **1.5** *Glycaemic Load:* **12**

FRAGRANT TUNA SALAD

Total Time: 30-35 min; 4 servings

---

300 g (11 oz) tuna steak (can use tinned tuna); 1 small sweet potato; 250 g (9 oz) green beans; 180 g (6.5 oz) chickpeas tinned in water (rinsed and drained); 70 g (2.5 oz) rocket lettuce; 60 g (2 oz) sultanas; 1 large onion; 12 cherry tomatoes; 25 g (1 oz) fresh coriander; 0.25 med lemon (juiced); 3 tsp ground mixed spice; 3 tbs olive oil; 2 tbs balsamic vinegar; salt and pepper (to taste)

1. Cook diced potatoes for 8-10 min on medium heat, or until cooked.
2. Chop green beans and steam for 8-10 min.
3. Mix potatoes, beans, lettuce, chickpeas, chopped onion and coriander, halved tomatoes and sultanas.
4. For the dressing, mix oil, vinegar, mixed spice, lemon juice, and salt and pepper to taste.
5. Use some of the dressing to coat tuna steaks and place them in a hot frying pan for 1-2 min on each side (combine the rest of the dressing with the salad).
6. Divide the salad into 4 servings and top with cooked tuna steak.

One serving contains: *Calories:* **359** *Total Carbohydrate (g):* **40** *Sugar (g):* **16** *Carbohydrate Portions:* **3.5** *Protein (g):* **27** *Total Fat (g):* **11** *Saturated Fat (g):* **2** *Unsaturated Fat (g):* **9** *Cholesterol (mg):* **23** *Fibre (g):* **8** *Sodium (mg):* **79** *Salt (g):* **0.2** *Calcium (mg):* **115** *Magnesium (mg):* **85** *Iron (mg):* **4** *Zinc (mg):* **2** *Glycaemic Load:* **18**

AVOCADO & SEA VEGETABLE SALAD

Total Time: 35 min; 4 servings

**100 g (3.5 oz) quinoa (can use amaranth or teff); 3 small avocados;
200 g (7 oz) broccoli; 220 g (8 oz) garden peas (frozen); 250 g (9 oz) melon
(galia or honeydew); 2 med red peppers; 25 g (1 oz) chia seeds; 6 spring onions;
3 tbs dried sea vegetables (arame, nori or other); 2 tbs sesame oil;
2 tsp dairy-free lemon grass paste; salt and pepper (to taste)**

1. Soak sea vegetables in cool water for 10-15 min.
2. Cook quinoa as per instructions on the packaging and rinse with cold water once cooked.
3. Cook peas as per instructions on the packaging.
4. Chop broccoli and steam for 5-6 min.
5. Mix cooked quinoa, sea vegetables, peas and broccoli with diced avocado, peppers and melon, chopped spring onions, oil, chia seeds, and lemon grass paste.
6. Divide into 4 servings, and add salt and pepper (to taste).

One serving contains: *Calories:* **400** *Total Carbohydrate (g):* **45** *Sugar (g):* **13**
Carbohydrate Portions: **3.5** *Protein (g):* **12** *Total Fat (g):* **21** *Saturated Fat (g):* **10**
Unsaturated Fat (g): **10** *Cholesterol (mg):* **0** *Fibre (g):* **16** *Sodium (mg):* **191** *Salt (g):* **0.5**
Calcium (mg): **113** *Magnesium (mg):* **115** *Iron (mg):* **4** *Zinc (mg):* **3** *Glycaemic Load:* **17**

ROOT VEGETABLE SALAD

Total Time: 30 min; 4 servings

---

4 small potatoes; 3 med carrots; 2 med parsnips; 0.25 med celeriac; 250 g (9 oz) garden peas (frozen); 8 med gherkins; 4 med eggs; 5 tsp mustard; 4 tbs eggless mayonnaise (refer to p. 174 for recipe); salt and pepper (to taste)

1. Put diced potatoes in a pan, cover with boiling water and cook 5 min on medium heat.
2. Add diced carrots, parsnips and celeriac and cook for further 10 min.
3. Check potatoes are cooked and drain.
4. Cook peas as per instructions on the packaging.
5. Combine cooked vegetables and peas with chopped gherkins, diced hard-boiled eggs (boil for 15-20 min), mustard and mayonnaise.
6. Divide into 4 servings
7. Add salt and pepper (to taste).

One serving contains: *Calories:* **360** *Total Carbohydrate (g):* **39** *Sugar (g):* **11**
Carbohydrate Portions: **3** *Protein (g):* **14** *Total Fat (g):* **17** *Saturated Fat (g):* **3**
Unsaturated Fat (g): **12** *Cholesterol (mg):* **227** *Fibre (g):* **10** *Sodium (mg):* **725** *Salt (g):* **1.8**
Calcium (mg): **134** *Magnesium (mg):* **81** *Iron (mg):* **4** *Zinc (mg):* **2** *Glycaemic Load:* **14**

GARDEN SALAD
Total Time: 30 min; 4 servings

**3 small avocados; 250 g (9 oz) cucumber; 200 g (7 oz) radishes;
200 g (7 oz) red cabbage (can use white); 2 med beetroots (cooked in water);
150 g (5.5 oz) sweetcorn tinned in water (drained); 30 g (1 oz) alfalfa sprouted
seeds; 6 spring onions; 60 g (2 oz) brown rice; 4 tbs plain soya yoghurt;
4 tbs eggless mayonnaise (refer to p. 174 for recipe);
15 g (0.5 oz) fresh mint; salt and pepper (to taste)**

1. Cook rice as per instructions on the packaging.
2. Combine cooked rice with finely shredded cabbage, sweetcorn, alfalfa seeds, diced cucumber, avocados, beetroots and radishes, chopped spring onions and mint, yoghurt and mayonnaise.
3. Divide into 4 servings
4. Add salt and pepper (to taste).

One serving contains: *Calories:* **368** *Total Carbohydrate (g):* **38** *Sugar (g):* **11**
Carbohydrate Portions: **3** *Protein (g):* **8** *Total Fat (g):* **23** *Saturated Fat (g):* **10**
Unsaturated Fat (g): **11** *Cholesterol (mg):* **0** *Fibre (g):* **12** *Sodium (mg):* **162** *Salt (g):* **0.4**
Calcium (mg): **125** *Magnesium (mg):* **93** *Iron (mg):* **3** *Zinc (mg):* **2** *Glycaemic Load:* **18**

PASTA SALAD WITH BASIL DRESSING

Total Time: 30 min; 4 servings

**250 g (9 oz) runner beans (or green beans); 2 med beetroot (cooked in water);
80 g (3 oz) gluten-free pasta; 1 med onion; 80 g (3 oz) baby spinach (or lettuce);
25 cherry tomatoes; 100 g (3.5 oz) pistachio nuts; 80 g (3 oz) back eye beans
tinned in water (rinsed and drained); 60 g (2 oz) sweetcorn tinned in water
(drained); salt and pepper (to taste)**
Basil dressing: **refer to p. 177 for recipe**

1. Cook pasta as per instructions on the packaging and rinse with cold water once cooked.
2. Soak pistachio nuts in warm water for 20 min.
3. Chop runner beans and steam for 8-10 min.
4. Combine pasta with cooked beans, black eye beans and sweetcorn, chopped onion and spinach, diced beetroot, halved tomatoes, pistachio nuts, and basil dressing.
5. Divide into 4 servings, and add salt and pepper to taste.

One serving contains: *Calories:* **396** *Total Carbohydrate (g):* **43** *Sugar (g):* **12**
Carbohydrate Portions: **4** *Protein (g):* **14** *Total Fat (g):* **21** *Saturated Fat (g):* **8**
Unsaturated Fat (g): **13** *Cholesterol (mg):* **0** *Fibre (g):* **10** *Sodium (mg):* **61** *Salt (g):* **0.15**
Calcium (mg): **124** *Magnesium (mg):* **137** *Iron (mg):* **6** *Zinc (mg):* **2** *Glycaemic Load:* **18**

PICKLED HERRING SALAD
Total Time: 25-30 min; 4 servings

---

280 g (10 oz) pickled herring (can use smoked mackerel); 300 g (11 oz) asparagus; 200 g (7 oz) broccoli; 120 g (5.5 oz) sweetcorn tinned in water (drained); 120 ml (4 fl oz) coconut milk; 70 g (2.5 oz) buckwheat; 1 med carrot; 1 small leek; 8 cherry tomatoes; 2 tbs mixed dried herbs; 2 tbs dried sea vegetables (arame, nori or other); 1 tbs apple cider vinegar; salt and pepper (to taste)

1. Soak sea vegetables in cool water for 10-15 min.
2. Steam roughly chopped broccoli and asparagus (trim the wide ends first) for 5-8 min.
3. Cook buckwheat as per instructions on the packaging.
4. Mix cooked broccoli and asparagus with sweetcorn and grated carrot.
5. Add cooked buckwheat mixed with finely chopped leek, seaweed, herbs, coconut milk and vinegar.
6. Top with slices of herring and tomatoes.
7. Divide into 4 servings, and add salt and pepper to taste.

One serving contains: *Calories:* **388** *Total Carbohydrate (g):* **36** *Sugar (g):* **12**
Carbohydrate Portions: **3** *Protein (g):* **19** *Total Fat (g):* **20** *Saturated Fat (g):* **6**
Unsaturated Fat (g): **11** *Cholesterol (mg):* **23** *Fibre (g):* **7** *Sodium (mg):* **687** *Salt (g):* **1.7**
Calcium (mg): **165** *Magnesium (mg):* **98** *Iron (mg):* **6** *Zinc (mg):* **2** *Glycaemic Load:* **18**

WATERMELON & TOFU SALAD

Total Time: 20 min; 4 servings

---

350 g (12.5 oz) firm tofu; 400 g (14 oz) watermelon (or other type of melon);
160 g (5.5 oz) rocket lettuce; 200 g (7 oz) cucumber; 160 g (5.5 oz) black pitted
olives; 160 g (5.5 oz) chickpeas tinned in water (rinsed and drained);
60 g (2 oz) pine nuts; 4 tbs olive oil; 2 tbs balsamic glaze; 6 spring onions;
salt and pepper (to taste)

1. Arrange diced watermelon, cucumber and tofu, olives and chickpeas on a bed of lettuce.
2. Sprinkle with chopped spring onions and pine nuts.
3. Dress with olive oil and balsamic glaze.
4. Divide into 4 servings
5. Add salt and pepper (to taste).

One serving contains: *Calories:* **424** *Total Carbohydrate (g):* **29** *Sugar (g):* **14**
Carbohydrate Portions: **2.5** *Protein (g):* **14** *Total Fat (g):* **30** *Saturated Fat (g):* **3**
Unsaturated Fat (g): **24** *Cholesterol (mg):* **0** *Fibre (g):* **5** *Sodium (mg):* **398** *Salt (g):* **1**
Calcium (mg): **122** *Magnesium (mg):* **102** *Iron (mg):* **5** *Zinc (mg):* **2** *Glycaemic Load:* **12**

CURRIED LAMB SALAD

Total Time: 25 min; 4 servings

---

320 g (11.5 oz) lean lamb; 200 g (7 oz) garden peas (frozen); 80 g (3 oz) amaranth (can use quinoa or teff); 150 g (5.5 oz) cucumber; 1 large pomegranate; 1 med red pepper; 1 med yellow pepper; 200 ml (7 oz) coconut milk; 70 g (2.5 oz) baby spinach; 3 tsp ground cinnamon; 2 tsp dried coriander; 2 tsp ground cumin; 2 tsp garlic powder; 1 tsp turmeric; 1 tbs coconut oil; salt and pepper (to taste)

1. Cook amaranth and peas as per instructions on the packaging.
2. Heat up coconut oil with spices in a frying pan, add diced lamb and coconut milk, and cook for 3-4 min on medium heat stirring frequently.
3. Add cooked amaranth.
4. Combine diced cucumber and peppers, chopped spinach, pomegranate seeds, cooked peas, and cooked lamb with amaranth.
5. Divide into 4 servings, and add salt and pepper to taste (serve warm).

* you can use Rogan Josh Masala powder in place of the spices

One serving contains: *Calories:* **445** *Total Carbohydrate (g):* **42** *Sugar (g):* **13** *Carbohydrate Portions:* **3.5** *Protein (g):* **26** *Total Fat (g):* **21** *Saturated Fat (g):* **11** *Unsaturated Fat (g):* **8** *Cholesterol (mg):* **59** *Fibre (g):* **10** *Sodium (mg):* **142** *Salt (g):* **0.4** *Calcium (mg):* **145** *Magnesium (mg):* **143** *Iron (mg):* **8** *Zinc (mg):* **5** *Glycaemic Load:* **16**

MINTY CELERIAC SALAD (SIDE SALAD)

Total Time: 15 min; 4 servings

0.75 med celeriac; 15 g (0.5 oz) fresh mint; 80 g (3 oz) walnuts; 60 g (2 oz) sultanas or raisins; 25 g (1 oz) alfalfa sprouted seeds; 6 tbs coconut milk; 0.5 med lemon (juiced); 0.5 tbs runny honey

1. Combine grated celeriac with lemon juice, coconut milk, honey and finely chopped mint.
2. Add sultanas, cracked walnuts, alfalfa seeds and mix together.
3. Divide into 4 servings.

* excellent addition to barbequed and grilled dishes

One serving contains: *Calories:* **261** *Total Carbohydrate (g):* **26** *Sugar (g):* **14** *Carbohydrate Portions:* **2.5** *Protein (g):* **5** *Total Fat (g):* **17** *Saturated Fat (g):* **4** *Unsaturated Fat (g):* **12** *Cholesterol (mg):* **0** *Fibre (g):* **4** *Sodium (mg):* **91** *Salt (g):* **0.2** *Calcium (mg):* **71** *Magnesium (mg):* **65** *Iron (mg):* **2** *Zinc (mg):* **1** *Glycaemic Load:* **12**

CARROT & APPLE SALAD (SIDE SALAD)

Total Time: 15 min; 4 servings

---

1 med carrots; 3 med apples; 0.5 med lemon (juiced); 3 tbs mustard seeds; 1 tbs runny honey; 1 tbs coconut oil

1. Heat up coconut oil in a frying pan, add mustard seeds and cover.
2. When seeds start popping, wait for a few seconds and remove from heat (keep the lid on).
3. Combine grated carrot and apple with lemon juice, honey and mustard seeds.
4. Divide into 4 servings.

* excellent addition to barbequed and grilled dishes

One serving contains: *Calories:* **146** *Total Carbohydrate (g):* **24** *Sugar (g):* **14** *Carbohydrate Portions:* **2.5** *Protein (g):* **3** *Total Fat (g):* **6** *Saturated Fat (g):* **0.5** *Unsaturated Fat (g):* **5** *Cholesterol (mg):* **0** *Fibre (g):* **4** *Sodium (mg):* **39** *Salt (g):* **0.1** *Calcium (mg):* **66** *Magnesium (mg):* **35** *Iron (mg):* **1** *Zinc (mg):* **1** *Glycaemic Load:* **7**

RED CABBAGE COLESLAW (SIDE SALAD)

Total Time: 15 min; 4 servings

0.25 red cabbage; 1 large carrot; 1 med red onion; 2 tbs plain soya yoghurt; 3 tbs eggless mayonnaise (refer to p. 174 for recipe); salt and pepper (to taste)

1. Combine finely shredded cabbage, grated carrot and chopped onion with yoghurt and mayonnaise.
2. Divide into 4 servings
3. Add salt and pepper (to taste).

* excellent addition to barbequed and grilled dishes, as well as sandwiches

One serving contains: *Calories:* **125** *Total Carbohydrate (g):* **12** *Sugar (g):* **6**
Carbohydrate Portions: **1** *Protein (g):* **2** *Total Fat (g):* **8** *Saturated Fat (g):* **1**
Unsaturated Fat (g): **6** *Cholesterol (mg):* **0** *Fibre (g):* **6** *Sodium (mg):* **102** *Salt (g):* **0.3**
Calcium (mg): **73** *Magnesium (mg):* **24** *Iron (mg):* **1** *Zinc (mg):* **0** *Glycaemic Load:* **5**

LIGHT MEALS

SPICED CHICKPEA BURGERS WITH GHERKIN DIP

Total Time: 35 min; 4 servings (1 serving = 2 burgers)

Burgers: **350 g (12.5 oz) chickpeas tinned in water (rinsed and drained);
1 large carrot; 1 large onion; 4 tbs gluten-free flour; 3 cloves garlic (peeled);
1 med egg (or egg replacer); 7 tsp ground mixed spice; 25 g (1 oz) fresh coriander;
5 tbs apple cider vinegar; 1 tbs coconut oil; 0.5 tsp sea salt; sunflower oil spray**
Dip: **250 g (9 oz) plain soya yoghurt; 6 med gherkins; 4 spring onions;
15 g (0.5 oz) fresh coriander; 1 tbs apple cider vinegar; salt and pepper (to taste)**

1. Sauté chopped onions in coconut oil for 3-4 min on medium heat.
2. Combine sautéed mix, mashed chickpeas, grated carrot, chopped coriander, flour, egg, spices, vinegar, gum and salt.
3. Divide mixture into 8 parts, form burgers and pan-fry on very low heat for 4-5 min on each side (use 8 sprays of sunflower oil each time).
4. For the dip, combine yoghurt with vinegar, finely chopped gherkins, spring onions and coriander, and salt and pepper to taste.

One serving contains: *Calories:* **292** *Total Carbohydrate (g):* **37** *Sugar (g):* **7**
Carbohydrate Portions: **3** *Protein (g):* **15** *Total Fat (g):* **10** *Saturated Fat (g):* **2**
Unsaturated Fat (g): **6** *Cholesterol (mg):* **57** *Fibre (g):* **10** *Sodium (mg):* **671** *Salt (g):* **1.7**
Calcium (mg): **209** *Magnesium (mg):* **76** *Iron (mg):* **4** *Zinc (mg):* **2** *Glycaemic Load:* **18**

ORIENTAL PRAWN OMELETTE

Total Time: 50 min; 4 servings (1 serving = 1 omelette)

Omelette: 8 med eggs; 200 ml (7 oz) unsweetened rice milk; sunflower oil spray
Filling: 320 g (11.5 oz) cooked prawns; 2 med carrots; 1 med red pepper;
100 g (3.5 oz) cabbage; 100 g (3.5 oz) bean sprouts; 4 spring onions;
80 g (3 oz) sweetcorn tinned in water (drained); 3 cloves garlic (peeled);
30 g (1 oz) sesame seeds; 1 tbs coconut oil; 2 tbs onion granules;
1 tbs garlic powder; 0.5 med lemon (juiced); salt and pepper (to taste)

1. Stir-fry grated carrot, crushed garlic, sweetcorn, chopped cabbage, spring onions and pepper, lemon juice, onion and garlic powder, in coconut oil for 15 min on medium heat (add salt and pepper to taste).
2. Add cleaned prawns, cook for further 5 min, then add sesame seeds.
3. Coat frying pan with sunflower oil spray (4 sprays each time).
4. Whisk eggs with rice milk and pan-fry omelettes for 2-3 min on each side on very low heat, or until golden brown (wait until well-set before turning).
5. Fill in omelettes with the prawn and vegetable mix.

One serving contains: *Calories:* **444** *Total Carbohydrate (g):* **25** *Sugar (g):* **7** *Carbohydrate Portions:* **2.5** *Protein (g):* **37** *Total Fat (g):* **22** *Saturated Fat (g):* **5** *Unsaturated Fat (g):* **14** *Cholesterol (mg):* **610** *Fibre (g):* **5** *Sodium (mg):* **697** *Salt (g):* **1.7** *Calcium (mg):* **285** *Magnesium (mg):* **108** *Iron (mg):* **5** *Zinc (mg):* **5** *Glycaemic Load:* **10**

QUICK PIZZA

Total Time: 45-50 min; 4 servings

Base: 90 g (3 oz) gluten-free self-raising flour; 30 g (1 oz) quinoa flour
(or self-raising flour); 1 med egg (or egg replacer); 3 tbs almond oil;
0.5 tsp sea salt; 7 tbs water
Topping: 120 g (4.5 oz) mushrooms; 1 med onion; 60 g spinach; 1 clove garlic
(peeled); 60 g (2 oz) tomato concentrate; 1 tbs mixed dried herbs; 1 tbs coconut oil;
70 g (2.5 oz) dairy-free grated mozzarella (optional); salt and pepper (to taste)

1. For the topping, sauté chopped onion, spinach and mushrooms with crushed garlic and herbs in coconut oil for 10 min on medium heat.
2. For the base, combine all the ingredients and knead for a few minutes.
3. Roll out the dough thin on parchment paper (approx. 25 cm diameter).
4. Spread tomato concentrate on the rolled out dough, apply topping and seasoning, and sprinkle with mozzarella.
5. Bake in a pre-heated oven for 20-25 min (gas mark 6).
6. Divide into 4 servings, and add salt and pepper to taste.

One serving contains: *Calories:* **344** *Total Carbohydrate (g):* **32** *Sugar (g):* **4**
Carbohydrate Portions: **3** *Protein (g):* **8** *Total Fat (g):* **20** *Saturated Fat (g):* **4**
Unsaturated Fat (g): **15** *Cholesterol (mg):* **57** *Fibre (g):* **4** *Sodium (mg):* **367** *Salt (g):* **0.9**
Calcium (mg): **60** *Magnesium (mg):* **49** *Iron (mg):* **2** *Zinc (mg):* **1** *Glycaemic Load:* **19**

CHICKEN PEPPERS

Total Time: 35 min; 4 servings (1 serving = 3 pepper halves)

---

320 g (11.5 oz) chicken breast; 3 med red peppers; 3 med yellow peppers; 50 g amaranth (can use quinoa or teff); 2 med onions; 100 g (3.5 oz) sweetcorn tinned in water (drained); 30 g (1 oz) tomato concentrate; 70 g (2.5 oz) spinach; 2 cloves garlic (peeled); 100 ml (3.5 fl oz) coconut milk; 1 tbs coconut oil; 2 tbs dried basil; 1 low-salt vegetable stock cube; olive oil spray; salt and pepper (to taste)

1. Cut peppers in half, remove seeds, spray with oil spray (2 sprays per each half), cover with foil, and place in a preheated oven for 20-25 min (gas mark 6).
2. Cook quinoa as per instructions on the packaging.
3. Sauté chopped onions and spinach, crushed garlic and basil in coconut oil for 5 min on medium heat.
4. Add diced chicken, cooked quinoa, sweetcorn, tomato concentrate, coconut milk, stock cube, and cook for further 8-10 min (check chicken is cooked).
5. Fill the pepper halves with the mixture, and add salt and pepper to taste.

One serving contains: *Calories:* **350** *Total Carbohydrate (g):* **38** *Sugar (g):* **10** *Carbohydrate Portions:* **3.5** *Protein (g):* **27** *Total Fat (g):* **11** *Saturated Fat (g):* **4** *Unsaturated Fat (g):* **5** *Cholesterol (mg):* **56** *Fibre (g):* **8** *Sodium (mg):* **97** *Salt (g):* **0.2** *Calcium (mg):* **134** *Magnesium (mg):* **126** *Iron (mg):* **5** *Zinc (mg):* **2** *Glycaemic Load:* **14**

STUFFED PANCAKES

Total Time: 45-50 min; 4 servings (1 serving = 2 pancakes)

Pancakes: 80 g (3 oz) plain gluten-free flour; 3 med eggs;
300 ml (10 fl oz) unsweetened almond milk; 100 ml (3.5 fl oz) water;
sunflower oil spray; pinch of salt
Filling: 2 small leeks; 1 med courgette, 1 med red pepper; 2 cloves garlic (peeled);
120 g (4.5 oz) black eye beans tinned in water (rinsed and drained);
30 g (1 oz) pumpkin seeds; 30 g (1 oz) sunflower seeds; 100 ml (3.5 fl oz) coconut
milk; 0.5 tbs coconut oil; 1 tbs mixed dried herbs; 0.5 tbs onion granules;
1 tbs apple cider vinegar; 0.25 tsp sea salt; pepper (to taste)

1. For the filling, sauté chopped leeks in coconut oil for 4-5 min on medium heat.
2. Add chopped pepper, grated courgette, crushed garlic, herbs, onion granules, beans, coconut milk, vinegar, salt and pepper, and cook for further 10 min on medium heat (add seeds at the end).
3. For the pancakes, mix all the ingredients, except oil, to form smooth batter.
4. Pan-fry pancakes for 1-2 min on each side on very low heat (use 3-4 sprays of sunflower oil each time), and fill them with the vegetable mix.

One serving contains: *Calories:* **415** *Total Carbohydrate (g):* **38** *Sugar (g):* **6**
Carbohydrate Portions: **3.5** *Protein (g):* **16** *Total Fat (g):* **22** *Saturated Fat (g):* **6**
Unsaturated Fat (g): **13** *Cholesterol (mg):* **170** *Fibre (g):* **6** *Sodium (mg):* **233** *Salt (g):* **0.6**
Calcium (mg): **205** *Magnesium (mg):* **157** *Iron (mg):* **6** *Zinc (mg):* **3** *Glycaemic Load:* **19**

SWEET POTATO FISH CAKES

Total Time: 35-45 min; 4 servings (1 serving = 1 large fish cake)

---

350 g (12.5 oz) cod; 1 large sweet potato; 2 med onions; 70 g (2.5 oz) sweetcorn tinned in water (drained); 2 med eggs (or egg replacers); 50 ml (2 fl oz) coconut milk; 2 cloves garlic (peeled); 25 g (1 oz) fresh coriander (chopped); 4 tbs apple cider vinegar; 3 tbs gluten-free flour; 1 tsp guar gum (or preferred alternative); 1 tbs coconut oil; 0.5 tsp sea salt;sunflower oil spray; a pinch of pepper

1. Cook diced potato for 8-10 min on medium heat, drain and mash.
2. Sauté chopped onions in coconut oil for 4-5 min on medium heat.
3. Cover cod in water with coconut milk and cook for 3-4 min.
4. Combine mashed potato with sautéed onions, cooked cod, sweetcorn, eggs, crushed garlic, coriander, flour, vinegar, gum, salt and pepper, thoroughly.
5. Coat frying pan with sunflower oil spray (use 6-8 sprays each time).
6. Pan-fry cakes for 3-4 min on each side on very low heat, or until golden brown (use two medium size frying pans at the same time to speed up the process; the mixture is sufficient for 4 large fish cakes).

One serving contains: Calories: 337 Total Carbohydrate (g): 37 Sugar (g): 8 Carbohydrate Portions: 3.5 Protein (g): 24 Total Fat (g): 10 Saturated Fat (g): 3 Unsaturated Fat (g): 6 Cholesterol (mg): 154 Fibre (g): 6 Sodium (mg): 451 Salt (g): 1.1 Calcium (mg): 85 Magnesium (mg): 71 Iron (mg): 2 Zinc (mg): 1.5 Glycaemic Load: 17

COURGETTE ROLLS WITH EGG MAYONNAISE

Total Time: 35-40 min; 4 servings (1 serving = 1 roll)

Rolls: **200 g (7 oz) self-raising gluten-free flour; 3 med eggs (or egg replacers); 2 med courgettes; 2 tbs flax seed; 2 tbs cumin seeds; 1 tsp gluten-free baking powder; 1 tsp sea salt**
Egg topping: **5 large eggs; 5 spring onions; 4 tbs gluten and dairy-free mayonnaise, or eggless mayonnaise (refer to p. 174 for recipe), salt and pepper (to taste)**

1. For the rolls, combine flour, eggs, grated courgette (squeeze all the juice out first), seeds, baking powder and salt, and knead for a few minutes (the mixture will remain sticky).
2. Divide mixture into 4 equal parts, form into balls, and place on a non-stick tray.
3. Bake in a pre-heated oven for 25 min (gas mark 6).
4. For the filling, combine diced hard-boiled eggs (boil for 15-20 min), chopped spring onion and mayonnaise, and add salt and pepper to taste.

* for alternatives, choose protein-based toppings (e.g. chicken) to keep glycaemic load low

One serving contains: *Calories:* **333** *Total Carbohydrate (g):* **31** *Sugar (g):* **2**
Carbohydrate Portions: **3** *Protein (g):* **13** *Total Fat (g):* **18** *Saturated Fat (g):* **4**
Unsaturated Fat (g): **12** *Cholesterol (mg):* **291** *Fibre (g):* **3** *Sodium (mg):* **647** *Salt (g):* **1.6**
Calcium (mg): **103** *Magnesium (mg):* **69** *Iron (mg):* **4** *Zinc (mg):* **2** *Glycaemic Load:* **19**

QUINOA MEATBALLS WITH TOMATO SALSA

Total Time: 60 min; (1 serving = 5 balls)

Meatballs: **320 g (11.5 oz) turkey mince; 60 g (2 oz) quinoa (can use teff or amaranth); 80 g (3 oz) sweetcorn tinned in water (drained); 1 large onion; 50 g (2 oz) gluten-free breadcrumbs; 3 tbs onion granules; 3 tbs dried chives; 2 tbs gluten-free flour; 1 tsp guar gum (or preferred alternative); 1 tbs coconut oil; 0.5 tsp sea salt; pepper (to taste); sunflower oil spray**
Salsa: **200g (7 oz) chopped tomatoes (tinned); 4 tbs coconut milk; 5 spring onions (finely chopped); salt and pepper (to taste)**

1. Cook quinoa as per instructions on the packaging.
2. Sauté finely chopped onion in coconut oil for 3-4 min on medium heat, then combine with cooked quinoa, mince, sweetcorn, onion granules, breadcrumbs, flour, chives, gum, salt and pepper.
3. Form the mixture into balls (20 smaller ones or 16 bigger ones) and bake on a tray (coated with oil spray) in a pre-heated oven for 35 min (gas mark 6).
4. For the salsa, mix all the ingredients and add salt and pepper to taste.

One serving contains: *Calories:* **304** *Total Carbohydrate (g):* **33** *Sugar (g):* **6** *Carbohydrate Portions:* **3** *Protein (g):* **25** *Total Fat (g):* **9** *Saturated Fat (g):* **3** *Unsaturated Fat (g):* **5** *Cholesterol (mg):* **56** *Fibre (g):* **5** *Sodium (mg):* **465** *Salt (g):* **1.2** *Calcium (mg):* **85** *Magnesium (mg):* **96** *Iron (mg):* **3** *Zinc (mg):* **3** *Glycaemic Load:* **17**

MINTY SPINACH LOAF

Total Time: 40-45 min; 4 servings

**150 g (5.5 oz) spinach; 2 med onions; 300 g (11 oz) plain soya yoghurt;
4 med eggs (or egg replacers); 7 tbs gluten-free self-raising flour;
3 cloves garlic (peeled); 30 g (1 oz) sesame seeds; 3 tbs dried mint;
1 tbs coconut oil; 1 tsp guar gum (or preferred alternative);
1 tsp sea salt; pinch of pepper (optional)**

1. Sauté crushed garlic, chopped onions and spinach in coconut oil for 4-5 min on medium heat, and combine with yoghurt, egg yolks, flour, mint, gum, salt and pepper, stirring (or whisking) until mixture thickens.
2. Beat egg whites (soft peaks) and gently fold into the mixture.
3. Transfer mixture into a non-stick baking tin, coated with oil spray (8 sprays) and a dusting of flour.
4. Sprinkle with sesame seeds and bake in a pre-heated oven for 25-30 min (gas mark 6), or until golden brown.
5. Divide into 4 servings and serve with a salad.

One serving contains: *Calories:* **301** *Total Carbohydrate (g):* **25** *Sugar (g):* **5**
Carbohydrate Portions: **2.5** *Protein (g):* **15** *Total Fat (g):* **16** *Saturated Fat (g):* **3**
Unsaturated Fat (g): **10** *Cholesterol (mg):* **227** *Fibre (g):* **6** *Sodium (mg):* **787** *Salt (g):* **2**
Calcium (mg): **294** *Magnesium (mg):* **97** *Iron (mg):* **6** *Zinc (mg):* **2** *Glycaemic Load:* **15**

SALMON MUSHROOMS

Total Time: 40 min; 4 servings (1 serving = 2 mushrooms)

**8 large flat mushrooms; 320 g (11.5 oz) salmon; 3 spring onions;
1 large onion; 3 cloves garlic (peeled); 40 g (1.5 oz) gluten-free breadcrumbs;
50 ml (2 fl oz) coconut milk; 1 tbs onion granules; 3 tbs dried dill;
1 low-salt vegetable stock cube; 2 tbs balsamic vinegar;
0.5 lemon (juiced); 1 tbs coconut oil; salt and pepper (to taste)**

1. Bake mushrooms in a pre-heated oven for 25 min (gas mark 7), covered with foil (add sprinkle of salt and pepper).
2. Sauté chopped onions and crushed garlic in coconut oil for 4-5 min on medium heat.
3. Add stock cube (dilute in small amount of hot water first), dill, onion granules, lemon juice, vinegar, coconut milk, and diced salmon, cook for further 2-3 min on medium heat, and mix in breadcrumbs once cooked.
4. Stuff mushrooms (remove any juice first) and bake for 5 min (gas mark 6).
5. Serve with a salad, and add salt and pepper to taste.

One serving contains: *Calories:* **311** *Total Carbohydrate (g):* **20** *Sugar (g):* **7**
Carbohydrate Portions: **2** *Protein (g):* **24** *Total Fat (g):* **16** *Saturated Fat (g):* **4**
Unsaturated Fat (g): **10** *Cholesterol (mg):* **40** *Fibre (g):* **3** *Sodium (mg):* **125** *Salt (g):* **0.3**
Calcium (mg): **108** *Magnesium (mg):* **65** *Iron (mg):* **3** *Zinc (mg):* **2** *Glycaemic Load:* **10**

CASHEW NUTLOAF
Total Time: 45-50 min; 4 servings

---

180 g (6.5 oz) cashew nuts; 4 med carrots; 1 large onion; 2 med eggs
(or egg replacers); 150 g (5.5 oz) garden peas (frozen); 4 cloves garlic (peeled);
100 ml (3.5 fl oz) unsweetened almond milk; 2 tbs gluten-free breadcrumbs;
15 g (0.5 oz) fresh parsley; 1 tbs onion granules; 0.5 med lemon (juiced);
2 tbs apple cider vinegar; 1 tbs coconut oil; 1 tsp guar gum (or preferred
alternative); 0.75 tsp sea salt; pinch of pepper (optional); sunflower oil spray

1. Sauté chopped onion in coconut oil for 4-5 min on medium heat.
2. Cook diced carrots for 10-15 min on medium heat, drain and mash.
3. Combine ground nuts, mashed carrots, sautéed onion, cooked peas (as per
   packaging instructions), crushed garlic, almond milk, breadcrumbs, eggs,
   chopped parsley, onion granules, lemon juice, vinegar, gum, salt and pepper.
4. Bake in a non-stick tin (coated with oil spray and a dusting flour) in
   a pre-heated oven for 30 min (gas mark 6), or until golden brown.
5. Divide into 4 servings, and serve with a salad.

One serving contains: *Calories:* **440** *Total Carbohydrate (g):* **39** *Sugar (g):* **11**
Carbohydrate Portions: **3.5** *Protein (g):* **16** *Total Fat (g):* **27** *Saturated Fat (g):* **5**
Unsaturated Fat (g): **19** *Cholesterol (mg):* **113** *Fibre (g):* **7** *Sodium (mg):* **639** *Salt (g):* **1.6**
Calcium (mg): **107** *Magnesium (mg):* **166** *Iron (mg):* **5** *Zinc (mg):* **4** *Glycaemic Load:* **15**

VEGETABLE LASAGNA
Total Time: 45-50 min; 4 servings

Lasagna: **6 gluten-free lasagne sheets; 250 g (9 oz) chestnut mushrooms; 250 g (9 oz) spinach; 1 med courgette; 150 g (5.5 oz) tinned chopped tomatoes; 1 med onion; 100 g (3.5 oz) dairy-free mozzarella (optional); 3 cloves garlic (peeled); 2 tbs mixed dried herbs; 0.5 tbs coconut oil** *White sauce:* **refer to p. 175 for details**

1. Sauté chopped onions and spinach, crushed garlic, grated courgette and herbs in coconut oil for 5-8 min on medium heat.
2. Pre-cook lasagne sheets (7-8 min, add some oil to prevent sticking).
3. To make white sauce, follow the instructions on p. 175.
4. Place two lasagne sheets in a square baking tin, then spread half the sautéed mix, half the tomatoes, and half the white sauce. Repeat.
5. Place the last two lasagne sheets on top, sprinkle with mozzarella and bake in a pre-heated oven for 20 min (gas mark 6).
6. Divide into 4 servings.

One serving contains: *Calories:* **350** *Total Carbohydrate (g):* **39** *Sugar (g):* **10** *Carbohydrate Portions:* **3.5** *Protein (g):* **12** *Total Fat (g):* **16** *Saturated Fat (g):* **8** *Unsaturated Fat (g):* **7** *Cholesterol (mg):* **0** *Fibre (g):* **8** *Sodium (mg):* **154** *Salt (g):* **0.4** *Calcium (mg):* **195** *Magnesium (mg):* **125** *Iron (mg):* **5** *Zinc (mg):* **2** *Glycaemic Load:* **19**

BEEF & ONION CAKE

Total Time: 40-45 min; 4 servings

---

320 g (11.5 oz) extra-lean beef mince; 2 med onions; 1 med carrot; 100 g (3.5 oz) garden peas (frozen); 50 ml (2 fl oz) unsweetened almond milk; 4 cloves garlic (peeled); 60 g (2 oz) dairy-free mozzarella (optional); 2 med eggs (or egg replacers); 5 tbs gluten-free self-raising flour; 2 tbs onion granules; 1 tbs ground bay leaf; 3 tbs almond oil; 1 tbs coconut oil; 0.5 tsp sea salt; pinch of pepper

1. Sauté chopped onions, crushed garlic, bay leaf, salt and pepper in coconut oil for 3-4 min on medium heat, add mince and cook for further 5 min.
2. Cook peas as per instructions on the packaging.
3. Combine the sautéed mix with cooked peas, grated carrot, almond milk, eggs, flour, and almond oil.
4. Transfer into a baking tin, sprayed with oil and coated with a dusting of flour.
5. Sprinkle mozzarella on top and bake 20-25 min (gas mark 6).
6. Divide into 4 servings.

One serving contains: *Calories:* **438** *Total Carbohydrate (g):* **27** *Sugar (g):* **6** *Carbohydrate Portions:* **2.5** *Protein (g):* **27** *Total Fat (g):* **25** *Saturated Fat (g):* **6** *Unsaturated Fat (g):* **17** *Cholesterol (mg):* **160** *Fibre (g):* **4** *Sodium (mg):* **431** *Salt (g):* **1** *Calcium (mg):* **93** *Magnesium (mg):* **54** *Iron (mg):* **4** *Zinc (mg):* **4** *Glycaemic Load:* **13**

MACKEREL JELLY

Total Time: 2 hrs 20 min (preparation only: 20 min); 4 servings

---

250 g (9 oz) smoked mackerel; 200 g (7 oz) garden peas (frozen); 1 med leek; 15 g (0.5 oz) fresh basil; 3 tbs eggless mayonnaise (refer to p. 174 for recipe); 1 portion gelatine (for 570 ml / 19 fl oz of liquid); 1 low-salt vegetable stock cube; 2 tbs apple cider vinegar; 0.3 tbs coconut oil; salt and pepper (to taste)

1. Sauté chopped leek in coconut oil for 3-4 min on medium heat.
2. Cook peas as per instructions on the packaging.
3. Place cooked peas, sautéed leek and chopped basil in a dish.
4. Combine mackerel with mayonnaise and vinegar to form paste, divide into 8 equal parts, and arrange on the bed of leeks, peas and basil.
5. Dilute gelatine and stock cube in 470 ml of hot water, pour slowly into the dish, and allow to set in the fridge for 2 hrs (or freezer for faster result).

* adding 90 g of salad potatoes per serving to this dish will increase the calorie value to 448 calories, carbohydrate portions to 2.5, and glycaemic load to 11

One serving contains: *Calories:* **378** *Total Carbohydrate (g):* **12** *Sugar (g):* **4**
Carbohydrate Portions: **1** *Protein (g):* **18** *Total Fat (g):* **29** *Saturated Fat (g):* **5**
Unsaturated Fat (g): **21** *Cholesterol (mg):* **66** *Fibre (g):* **4** *Sodium (mg):* **581** *Salt (g):* **1.5**
Calcium (mg): **61** *Magnesium (mg):* **50** *Iron (mg):* **2.5** *Zinc (mg):* **1** *Glycaemic Load:* **4**

MEAT LOAF WITH SPINACH & MUSHROOM FILLING

Total Time: 50 min; 4 servings

Meatloaf: 320g (11 .5 oz) extra lean beef mince; 5 tbs gluten-free flour;
30 g (1 oz) sunflower seeds; 60 g (2 oz) sweetcorn tinned in water (drained);
2 tbs dried basil; 1 tbs onion granules; 1 tsp guar gum (or preferred alternative);
0.5 tsp sea salt; pinch of pepper
Filling: 150 g (5.5 oz) fresh mushrooms; 150 g (5.5 oz) spinach; 2 cloves garlic
(peeled); 1 large onion; 2 tbs gluten-free breadcrumbs; 1 small egg; 1 tbs coconut oil
Basil dressing: refer to p. 177 for details

1. Combine mince, flour, seeds, sweetcorn, basil, onion granules, gum, salt and pepper, and divide the mixture in half.
2. Sauté chopped onion, mushrooms and spinach, and crushed garlic in coconut oil for 5-7 min on medium heat, then combine with egg and breadcrumbs.
3. Place half of the mince mixture in a non-stick baking tin, top with the filling, and the rest of the mince mixture, and bake for 35 min (gas mark 6).
4. Allow to cool before cutting (you may need to reheat once cut).
5. Serve with basil dressing (divide into 4 servings).

One serving contains: *Calories:* **407** *Total Carbohydrate (g):* **29** *Sugar (g):* **6**
Carbohydrate Portions: **2.5** *Protein (g):* **27** *Total Fat (g):* **21** *Saturated Fat (g):* **9**
Unsaturated Fat (g): **10** *Cholesterol (mg):* **93** *Fibre (g):* **5** *Sodium (mg):* **459** *Salt (g):* **1.2**
Calcium (mg): **142** *Magnesium (mg):* **125** *Iron (mg):* **7** *Zinc (mg):* **5** *Glycaemic Load:* **15**

MAIN MEALS

MAROCCAN PORK

Total Time: 40 min; 4 servings

**320 g (11.5 oz) lean pork; 200 g (7 oz) broccoli; 1 med courgette; 1 med carrot;
1 large red onion; 150 g (5.5 oz) chickpeas tinned in water (rinsed and drained);
2 small red peppers; 1 small yellow pepper; 70 g (2.5 oz) dried apricots;
150 g (5.5 oz) tomato concentrate; 100 ml (3.5 fl oz) coconut milk; 4 cloves garlic
(peeled); 1 tbs coconut oil; 2 tsp ground cinnamon; 2 tsp ground cloves;
2 tsp dried coriander; 1 tsp ginger powder; 1 low-salt vegetable
stock cube; salt and cayenne pepper (to taste)**

1. Sauté chopped onion with crushed garlic and spices in coconut oil for 3-4 min on medium heat.
2. Add stock cube, chopped vegetables, chopped apricots and chickpeas, and cook for 15-20 min on low heat (covered), stirring occasionally.
3. Add diced pork, tomato concentrate and coconut milk, and cook for further 5-7 min.
4. Divide into 4 servings, and add salt and cayenne pepper to taste.

One serving contains: *Calories:* **380** *Total Carbohydrate (g):* **39** *Sugar (g):* **20**
Carbohydrate Portions: **3.5** *Protein (g):* **29** *Total Fat (g):* **14** *Saturated Fat (g):* **5**
Unsaturated Fat (g): **7** *Cholesterol (mg):* **50** *Fibre (g):* **11** *Sodium (mg):* **180** *Salt (g):* **0.5**
Calcium (mg): **156** *Magnesium (mg):* **110** *Iron (mg):* **5** *Zinc (mg):* **4** *Glycaemic Load:* **18**

LEMON & TARRAGON SALMON

Total Time: 25 min; 4 servings

**400 g (14 oz) salmon; 250 g (9 oz) mangetout; 220 g (8 oz) garden peas;
150 g (5.5 oz) gluten-free pasta; 100 ml (3.5 fl oz) coconut milk (can use rice cream);
2 large onions; 1 med courgette; 15 g (0.5 oz) fresh tarragon (or 2 tbs dried);
6 cloves garlic (peeled); 1 med lemon (juiced); 1 large orange (juiced);
1.5 tbs coconut oil; 1 low-salt vegetable stock cube; salt and pepper (to taste)**

1. Sauté chopped onions with crushed garlic in 1 tbs of coconut oil for 3-4 min on medium heat.
2. Add stock cube, chopped mangetout, grated courgette, peas, lemon and orange juice, and cook for 10 min on low heat (covered).
3. Cook pasta separately, as per instructions on the packaging.
4. Pan-fry salmon in 0.5 tbs of coconut oil for 6-8 min on low heat (covered).
5. Combine vegetable mix with the pasta and add finely chopped tarragon.
6. Divide into 4 servings, top with pieces of cooked salmon, and add salt and pepper to taste.

One serving contains: *Calories:* **361** *Total Carbohydrate (g):* **38** *Sugar (g):* **8**
Carbohydrate Portions: **3.5** *Protein (g):* **21** *Total Fat (g):* **15** *Saturated Fat (g):* **4**
Unsaturated Fat (g): **9** *Cholesterol (mg):* **33** *Fibre (g):* **7** *Sodium (mg):* **81** *Salt (g):* **0.2**
Calcium (mg): **83** *Magnesium (mg):* **94** *Iron (mg):* **3** *Zinc (mg):* **2** *Glycaemic Load:* **19**

SAUERKRAUT & MUSHROOM STEW

Total Time: 45 min; 4 servings

---

600 g (21.5 oz) sauerkraut; 0.5 med white cabbage; 200 g (7 oz) chestnut mushrooms; 1 large onion; 25 g (1 oz) dried wild mushrooms; 1 med carrot; 3 small potatoes; 150 g (5.5 oz) garden peas (frozen); 5 cloves garlic (peeled); 1 tbs coconut oil; 2 tbs marjoram; 1 tbs onion granules; 1 tbs garlic powder; 200 ml (7 oz) water; 1 low-salt vegetable stock cube; salt and pepper (to taste)

1. Cover dried mushrooms in hot water and soak for 10 min.
2. Sauté chopped onion in coconut oil for 3-4 min on medium heat.
3. Add chopped sauerkraut (rinse first), cabbage, carrot and mushrooms (fresh and soaked), crushed garlic, stock cube, marjoram, garlic powder, onion granules, cooked peas (as per packaging instructions), and water (boiled), and cook for 25 min on low heat (covered), stirring occasionally.
4. Cook diced potatoes separately (10-15 min on medium heat, or until cooked), then add to the stew.
5. Divide into 4 servings, and add salt and pepper to taste.

One serving contains: *Calories:* **247** *Total Carbohydrate (g):* **48** *Sugar (g):* **14**
Carbohydrate Portions: **4** *Protein (g):* **10** *Total Fat (g):* **5** *Saturated Fat (g):* **1**
Unsaturated Fat (g): **3** *Cholesterol (mg):* **0** *Fibre (g):* **15** *Sodium (mg):* **1080** *Salt (g):* **2.7**
Calcium (mg): **175** *Magnesium (mg):* **87** *Iron (mg):* **6** *Zinc (mg):* **2** *Glycaemic Load:* **18**

TURKEY STIR-FRY WITH PEANUT SAUCE

Total Time: 30 min; 4 servings

**320 g (11.5 oz) turkey; 200 g (7 oz) mangetout; 150 g (5.5 oz) baby corn;
150 g (5.5 oz) bean sprouts; 150 g (5.5 oz) chestnut mushrooms;
70 g (2.5 oz) brown rice; 2 med red peppers; 80 g (3 oz) peanut butter;
70 ml (2.5 fl oz) coconut milk; 5 spring onions; 15 g (0.5 oz) fresh mint
(or 2 tbs dried); 1.5 tbs sesame seeds; 1 tbs apple cider vinegar;
1 tbs coconut oil; 100 ml (3.5 fl oz) water; salt and pepper (to taste)**

1. Cook rice as per instructions on the packaging.
2. For the peanut sauce, mix peanut butter, coconut milk, vinegar and water.
3. Stir-fry bean sprouts, chopped mangetout, corn, mushrooms, spring onions and peppers in coconut oil for 10 min on medium heat (covered).
4. Add diced turkey and peanut sauce, and cook covered for 7-8 min on low heat (checked turkey is cooked through).
5. Add cooked rice, sesame seeds and chopped mint.
6. Divide into 4 servings, and add salt and pepper to taste.

One serving contains: *Calories:* **446** *Total Carbohydrate (g):* **37** *Sugar (g):* **11**
Carbohydrate Portions: **3.5** *Protein (g):* **33** *Total Fat (g):* **21** *Saturated Fat (g):* **11**
Unsaturated Fat (g): **8** *Cholesterol (mg):* **56** *Fibre (g):* **8** *Sodium (mg):* **165** *Salt (g):* **0.4**
Calcium (mg): **107** *Magnesium (mg):* **153** *Iron (mg):* **4** *Zinc (mg):* **3** *Glycaemic Load:* **18**

VEGETABLE & LENTIL STEW

Total Time: 40-45 min; 4 servings

0.5 med cabbage; 1 med sweet potato; 1 large onion; 1 med carrot; 1 small leek; 1 med courgette; 70 g (2.5 oz) red lentils; 4 cloves garlic (peeled); 100 g (3.5 oz) tomato concentrate; 1 tbs coconut oil; 25 g (1 oz) fresh parsley; 4 bay leaves; 1 low-salt vegetable stock cube; 1 tbs dried parsley; 1 tbs onion granules; 1 tbs garlic powder; 600 ml (20 fl oz) water; salt and pepper (to taste)

1. Sauté chopped onion, leek, crushed garlic in coconut oil for 3-4 min on medium heat.
2. Add stock cube, chopped vegetables, lentils (rinse thoroughly first), bay leaves, dried parsley, onion granules, garlic powder, tomato concentrate and water (boiled), and cook for 25 min on low heat (covered). Stir occasionally.
3. Add chopped parsley.
4. Divide into 4 servings, and add salt and pepper to taste.

One serving contains: *Calories:* **259** *Total Carbohydrate (g):* **47** *Sugar (g):* **15** *Carbohydrate Portions:* **4** *Protein (g):* **10** *Total Fat (g):* **5** *Saturated Fat (g):* **0** *Unsaturated Fat (g):* **4** *Cholesterol (mg):* **0** *Fibre (g):* **11** *Sodium (mg):* **149** *Salt (g):* **0.4** *Calcium (mg):* **146** *Magnesium (mg):* **77** *Iron (mg):* **5** *Zinc (mg):* **2** *Glycaemic Load:* **19**

CORN PANCAKES WITH CORIANDER CHICKEN

Total Time: 45-50 min; 4 servings (1 serving = 1 large pancake)

Pancakes: 240 g (8.5 oz) sweetcorn tinned in water; 4 small potatoes; 4 med eggs (or egg replacers); 100 ml (3.5 fl oz) unsweetened almond milk; 1 tbs gluten-free flour; 5 tsp dried coriander; 1 tsp guar gum; 0.5 tsp sea salt; sunflower oil spray
Topping: 320 g (11.5 oz) chicken breast; 300 g (11 oz) fresh mushrooms; 1 med leek; 2 med red peppers; 80 ml (2.5 fl oz) coconut milk; 15 g (0.5 oz) fresh coriander; 2 cloves garlic (peeled); 1 tbs apple cider vinegar; 2 tbs dried coriander; 1 tbs coconut oil; salt and pepper (to taste)

1. Sauté crushed garlic, chopped leek and mushrooms in coconut oil for 3-4 min.
2. Add diced chicken and peppers, dried coriander, coconut milk and vinegar, cook for further 8-10 min, then add chopped coriander.
3. To make pancakes, cook diced potatoes for 15 min (drain and mash), blend with the other ingredients until smooth, then pan-fry pancakes for 3-4 min on each side on very low heat (use 4-5 oil sprays each time), or until golden brown. Use two frying pans at the same time to speed the process up.
4. Top pancakes with chicken mix, and add salt and pepper to taste.

One serving contains: *Calories:* **447** *Total Carbohydrate (g):* **43** *Sugar (g):* **9**
Carbohydrate Portions: **4** *Protein (g):* **34** *Total Fat (g):* **16** *Saturated Fat (g):* **5**
Unsaturated Fat (g): **9** *Cholesterol (mg):* **283** *Fibre (g):* **8** *Sodium (mg):* **449** *Salt (g):* **1.1**
Calcium (mg): **155** *Magnesium (mg):* **113** *Iron (mg):* **6** *Zinc (mg):* **3** *Glycaemic Load:* **18**

VEGETABLE BAKE

Total Time: 45-50 min; 4 servings

---

1 large onion; 100 g (3.5 oz) broccoli; 100 g (3.5 oz) mangetout; 1 large carrot;
80 g (3 oz) sweetcorn tinned in water (drained); 1 med courgette; 3 cloves garlic
(peeled); 60 g (2 oz) gluten-free flour; 250 ml (8.5 oz) rice milk; 4 med eggs;
3 tbs mixed Italian herbs; 1 tbs onion granules; 1 tbs garlic powder;
1 tbs coconut oil; 1 low-salt vegetable stock cube; 0.5 tsp sea salt

1. Chop carrot and steam for 5 min (or blanch), then add chopped courgette, mangetout and broccoli, and steam for further 5 min.
2. Sauté chopped onion and crushed garlic in coconut oil for 3-4 min on medium heat, add salt, onion granules, garlic powder, mixed herbs, and stock cube (dilute in 2 tbs of hot water first).
3. Whisk flour with eggs and rice milk.
4. Place sautéed mix, steamed vegetables and sweetcorn in baking tray, pour in egg mixture, and bake for 25-30 min (gas mark 6).
5. Divide into 4 servings.

One serving contains: *Calories:* **303** *Total Carbohydrate (g):* **37** *Sugar (g):* **7**
Carbohydrate Portions: **3.5** *Protein (g):* **13** *Total Fat (g):* **12** *Saturated Fat (g):* **2**
Unsaturated Fat (g): **7** *Cholesterol (mg):* **227** *Fibre (g):* **5** *Sodium (mg):* **433** *Salt (g):* **1**
Calcium (mg): **144** *Magnesium (mg):* **61** *Iron (mg):* **4** *Zinc (mg):* **2** *Glycaemic Load:* **19**

CAULIFLOWER & SPINACH CURRY
Total Time: 40-45 min; 4 servings

**0.5 med cauliflower; 200 g (7 oz) spinach; 1 large onion; 2 med carrots;
100 g (3.5 oz) red lentils; 3 cloves garlic (peeled); 200 ml (7 fl oz) coconut milk;
25 g (1 oz) fresh coriander; 1 tbs coconut oil; 1 low-salt vegetable stock cube;
3 tsp allspice; 2 tsp dried coriander; 2 tsp turmeric; 2 tsp ginger powder;
2 tsp cumin; cayenne pepper (optional); 600 ml (20 fl oz) water;
salt and cayenne pepper (to taste)**

1. Sauté chopped onion, crushed garlic and spices in coconut oil for 3-4 min on medium heat.
2. Add stock cube, chopped vegetables, lentils (rinse thoroughly first) and water (boiled), and cook for 25 min on low heat (covered). Stir occasionally.
3. Add coconut milk and chopped coriander.
4. Divide into 4 servings, and add salt and cayenne pepper to taste.

One serving contains: *Calories:* **313** *Total Carbohydrate (g):* **38** *Sugar (g):* **7**
Carbohydrate Portions: **3** *Protein (g):* **13** *Total Fat (g):* **14** *Saturated Fat (g):* **8**
Unsaturated Fat (g): **5** *Cholesterol (mg):* **0** *Fibre (g):* **11** *Sodium (mg):* **113** *Salt (g):* **0.3**
Calcium (mg): **165** *Magnesium (mg):* **123** *Iron (mg):* **8** *Zinc (mg):* **2** *Glycaemic Load:* **15**

RED CABBAGE BEEF WITH HERB POTATOES

Total Time: 1 hr 45 min; 4 servings

Beef stew: 320 g (11.5 oz) lean beef; 0.5 med red cabbage; 1 large red onion;
4 med apples; 70 ml (2.5 fl oz) coconut milk; 3 tbs redcurrant jelly; 0.5 med lemon
(juiced); 2 tsp ground cinnamon; 1 tsp ground cloves; 1 tsp ground nutmeg;
1 tbs coconut oil; 150 ml (5 fl oz) water; salt and pepper (to taste)
Herb potatoes: 4 small potatoes; 1 tbs coconut oil;
2 tbs mixed dried herbs; salt and pepper (to taste)

1. Sauté chopped onion in 1 tbs of coconut oil for 3-4 min on medium heat.
2. Add diced beef, season and cook for 2-3 min to seal; then add chopped
   red cabbage, grated apples, lemon juice, jelly, spices and water, and cook
   for 1 hr and 30 min on low heat (covered). Add coconut milk once cooked.
3. Place diced potatoes in a baking tray and combine with herbs, sprinkle of salt
   and pepper, and melted coconut oil (melt in a separate pan), cover with foil
   and bake for 30 min (gas mark 6), then uncover and bake for further 15 min.
4. Divide into 4 servings, and add salt and pepper to taste.

One serving contains: *Calories:* **440** *Total Carbohydrate (g):* **51** *Sugar (g):* **24**
Carbohydrate Portions: **4.5** *Protein (g):* **20** *Total Fat (g):* **19** *Saturated Fat (g):* **7**
Unsaturated Fat (g): **11** *Cholesterol (mg):* **48** *Fibre (g):* **9** *Sodium (mg):* **104** *Salt (g):* **0.3**
Calcium (mg): **143** *Magnesium (mg):* **82** *Iron (mg):* **6** *Zinc (mg):* **4** *Glycaemic Load:* **18**

THAI PRAWNS WITH PECANS
Total Time: 30-35 min; 4 servings

**320 g (11.5 oz) cooked prawns; 260 g (9.5 oz) cooked rice noodles;
200 g (7 oz) mangetout; 150 g (5.5 oz) baby corn; 2 med red peppers;
2 med carrots; 6 spring onions; 150 ml (5 fl oz) coconut milk;
60 g (2 oz) pecan nuts; 3 cloves garlic (peeled); 1 tbs ground ginger;
2 tsp dairy-free lemon grass paste; 0.5 tbs coconut oil;
salt and cayenne pepper (to taste)**

1. Stir-fry chopped mangetout, baby corn, spring onions and peppers, grated carrots, and crushed garlic in coconut oil for 10-12 min on medium heat (covered).
2. Add cleaned prawns, noodles, coconut milk, ginger, and lemon grass paste, and cook for further 5-7 min on low heat.
3. Add pecan nuts.
4. Divide into 4 servings, and add salt and cayenne pepper to taste.

One serving contains: *Calories:* **450** *Total Carbohydrate (g):* **40** *Sugar (g):* **10**
Carbohydrate Portions: **3.5** *Protein (g):* **26** *Total Fat (g):* **21** *Saturated Fat (g):* **7**
Unsaturated Fat (g): **12** *Cholesterol (mg):* **156** *Fibre (g):* **8** *Sodium (mg):* **575** *Salt (g):* **1.4**
Calcium (mg): **161** *Magnesium (mg):* **120** *Iron (mg):* **4** *Zinc (mg):* **4** *Glycaemic Load:* **18**

MINTED LAMB POTATO ROSTIES

Total Time: 45-50 min; 4 servings (4 large rosties)

Rosties: 8 small potatoes; 3 med eggs (or egg replacers); 2 tbs gluten-free flour;
1 tsp guar gum (or preferred alternative); 0.5 tsp sea salt; sunflower oil spray
Filling: 320 g (11.5 oz) lean lamb; 160 g (5.5 oz) peas (frozen); 2 med onions;
2 med carrots; 120 g (4.5 oz) plain soya yoghurt (or rice cream); 3 cloves garlic
(peeled); 2 tbs dried mint; 1 low-salt vegetable stock cube; 1 tbs coconut oil;
1 tbs ground flax seed; 350 ml (12 fl oz) water; salt and pepper (to taste)

1. Sauté chopped onion and crushed garlic in coconut oil for 3-4 min, add diced lamb and cook for further 1-2 min on medium heat to seal.
2. Add grated carrots, mint, stock cube, water (boiled), salt and pepper (to taste), and continue to cook for 2-3 min, stirring occasionally.
3. Mix in yoghurt, cooked peas (as per packaging instructions) and flax seed.
4. To make rosties, mix grated potatoes with eggs, flour, gum and salt.
5. Pan-fry for 3-4 min on each side on low heat using 4-5 oil sprays each time (use two frying pans at the same time), and fill with lamb stew.

One serving contains: *Calories:* **429** *Total Carbohydrate (g):* **39** *Sugar (g):* **8**
Carbohydrate Portions: **3.5** *Protein (g):* **29** *Total Fat (g):* **17** *Saturated Fat (g):* **5**
Unsaturated Fat (g): **10** *Cholesterol (mg):* **229** *Fibre (g):* **7** *Sodium (mg):* **510** *Salt (g):* **1.3**
Calcium (mg): **152** *Magnesium (mg):* **87** *Iron (mg):* **5** *Zinc (mg):* **4** *Glycaemic Load:* **17**

   (Ca) (Mg) (Fe) (Zn)

GRILLED VEGETABLES & VENISON SPAGHETTI

Total Time: 60 min; 4 servings

---

320 g (11.5 oz) venison (can use lean beef or lamb); 1 large aubergine; 75 g (2.5 oz) gluten-free spaghetti; 1 large red onion; 2 med red peppers; 250 g (9 oz) asparagus; 400 g (14.5 oz) chopped tomatoes (tinned); 100 ml (3.5 fl oz) coconut milk; 4 cloves garlic (peeled); 3 tbs mixed dried herbs; 2 tbs coconut oil; salt and pepper (to taste)

1. Mix diced vegetables with crushed garlic, herbs, seasoning and 1.5 tbs of melted coconut oil (melt in a separate pan), place in a baking tray and bake covered with foil for 30 min, uncover, stir, and bake for further 15-20 min.
2. Cook spaghetti as per instructions on the packaging.
3. Pan-fry diced venison in 0.5 tbs of coconut oil for 2-3 min on medium heat.
4. Heat up chopped tomatoes in a saucepan.
5. Add coconut milk, venison and cooked spaghetti, and mix together.
6. Divide into 4 servings, top with grilled vegetables, and add salt and pepper to taste.

One serving contains: *Calories:* **356** *Total Carbohydrate (g):* **33** *Sugar (g):* **12** *Carbohydrate Portions:* **3** *Protein (g):* **25** *Total Fat (g):* **15** *Saturated Fat (g):* **5** *Unsaturated Fat (g):* **7** *Cholesterol (mg):* **14** *Fibre (g):* **9** *Sodium (mg):* **53** *Salt (g):* **0.1** *Calcium (mg):* **108** *Magnesium (mg):* **83** *Iron (mg):* **6** *Zinc (mg):* **1.5** *Glycaemic Load:* **18**

WINTER VEGETABLE HADDOCK

Total Time: 30-35 min; 4 servings

---

320 g (11.5 oz) haddock (can use cod); 2 med onions; 3 med carrots;
2 small parsnips; 0.25 med celeriac; 5 small potatoes; 3 cloves garlic (peeled);
50 g (2 oz) tomato concentrate; 50 ml (2 fl oz) unsweetened rice milk;
25 g (1 oz) fresh coriander; 3 tsp dried coriander; 2 tbs coconut oil;
1 low-salt vegetable stock cube; salt and pepper (to taste)

1. Sauté chopped onion and crushed garlic in 1 tbs of coconut oil for 3-4 min on medium heat.
2. Add tomato concentrate, stock cube (dilute in a bit of water first), 2 tsp of dried coriander, grated carrots, parsnips and celeriac, and cook for 10 min on medium heat (stirring occasionally), then add chopped coriander.
3. Cook diced potatoes for 15 min, drain and mash with rice milk.
4. Pan-fry haddock in 1 tbs of coconut oil on medium heat for 2-3 min on each side, with 1 tsp of dried coriander, and a pinch of salt and pepper.
5. Divide into 4 servings, and add salt and pepper to taste if required.

One serving contains: *Calories:* **326** *Total Carbohydrate (g):* **43** *Sugar (g):* **10**
Carbohydrate Portions: **4** *Protein (g):* **22** *Total Fat (g):* **9** *Saturated Fat (g):* **1**
Unsaturated Fat (g): **7** *Cholesterol (mg):* **31** *Fibre (g):* **8** *Sodium (mg):* **174** *Salt (g):* **0.4**
Calcium (mg): **140** *Magnesium (mg):* **81** *Iron (mg):* **3** *Zinc (mg):* **1.5** *Glycaemic Load:* **16**

SPINACH & ASPARAGUS QUINOA

Total Time: 30 min; 4 servings

---

300 g (11 oz) spinach; 300 g (11 oz) asparagus; 200 g (7 oz) garden peas (frozen); 2 med courgettes; 150 g (5.5 oz) chestnut mushrooms; 250 ml (8.5 fl oz) coconut milk; 80 g (3 oz) quinoa (can use teff or amaranth); 80 g (3 oz) cashew nuts; 1 med red onion; 3 cloves garlic (peeled); 15 g (0.5 oz) dried sea vegetables (arame, wakame or nori); 4 tbs apple cider vinegar; 3 tbs mixed dried herbs; 25 g (1 oz) fresh coriander; 0.5 tbs coconut oil; salt and pepper (to taste)

1. Cook quinoa and peas as per instructions on the packaging.
2. Soak sea vegetables in cool water for 10-15 min.
3. Sauté chopped onion and crushed garlic in coconut oil for 3-4 min on medium heat, add herbs, grated courgettes, chopped mushrooms, spinach, seaweed, and asparagus (trim the wide ends first), and cook for 10-15 min on medium heat stirring occasionally.
4. Add cooked peas and quinoa, coconut milk, vinegar, cashew nuts, chopped coriander, salt and pepper (to taste), and cook for further 1-2 min.

One serving contains: *Calories:* **436** *Total Carbohydrate (g):* **42** *Sugar (g):* **11** *Carbohydrate Portions:* **3.5** *Protein (g):* **17** *Total Fat (g):* **24** *Saturated Fat (g):* **11** *Unsaturated Fat (g):* **10** *Cholesterol (mg):* **0** *Fibre (g):* **11** *Sodium (mg):* **208** *Salt (g):* **0.5** *Calcium (mg):* **203** *Magnesium (mg):* **235** *Iron (mg):* **10** *Zinc (mg):* **4** *Glycaemic Load:* **19**

ONION & SMOKED MACKEREL CAKE

Total Time: 60 min; 6 servings

Cake: 4 med onions; 240 g (8.5 oz) chickpeas tinned in water (rinsed and drained); 3 med eggs (or egg replacers); 150 ml (5 fl oz) unsweetened almond milk; 100 g (3.5 oz) gluten-free flour; 1 low-salt vegetable stock cube; 1 tbs onion granules; 1 tbs coconut oil; 0.25 tsp sea salt; sunflower oil spray
Filling: 320 g (11.5 oz) smoked mackerel fillet; 80 ml (3 fl oz) coconut milk; 1 med lemon (juiced); 15 g (0.5 oz) chopped fresh parsley; 3 tbs balsamic vinegar; pepper

1. Sauté chopped onion in coconut oil for 3-4 min on medium heat, add stock cube (dilute in 2 tbs of hot water first), salt and onion granules.
2. Combine sautéed mix with mashed chickpeas, flour, eggs and milk thoroughly.
3. Bake for 30 min (gas mark 6), in a tin coated with oil spray and a dusting of flour.
4. For the filling, combine all the ingredients and place in the fridge to chill.
5. Allow cake to cool, slice through, fill, then reheat if required.
6. Divide into 6 servings.

One serving contains: *Calories:* **437** *Total Carbohydrate (g):* **32** *Sugar (g):* **6** *Carbohydrate Portions:* **3** *Protein (g):* **20** *Total Fat (g):* **26** *Saturated Fat (g):* **6** *Unsaturated Fat (g):* **16** *Cholesterol (mg):* **169** *Fibre (g):* **5** *Sodium (mg):* **550** *Salt (g):* **1.4** *Calcium (mg):* **115** *Magnesium (mg):* **65** *Iron (mg):* **3** *Zinc (mg):* **2** *Glycaemic Load:* **17**

    (Ca) (Mg) (Fe) (Zn)

DESSERTS

CARROT CAKE

Total Time: 45 min; 12 servings (1 serving = 1 piece)

**150 g (5.5 oz) gluten-free self-raising flour; 50 g (2 oz) gluten-free oats;
3 med carrots; 4 med eggs (or egg replacers); 200 ml (7 fl oz) unsweetened
almond milk; 120 g (4.5 oz) mixed dried fruit; 100 g (3.5 oz) pecan nuts;
5 tbs runny honey; 5 tsp ground mixed spice; 2 tsp cinnamon;
1 tsp gluten-free baking powder; zest of 1 large orange (grated);
28 servings stevia; sunflower oil spray**

1. Nuts should be soaked overnight but this is not essential to the recipe.
2. Combine flour, oats, grated carrots and orange zest, egg yolks, almond milk, honey, spices, baking powder and stevia (stir or whisk).
3. Beat egg whites (soft peaks).
4. Gently fold egg whites, mixed dried fruit and chopped nuts into the mixture.
5. Coat a non-stick baking tin with oil spray (8 sprays) and a dusting of flour.
6. Bake in a pre-heated oven for 30 min (gas mark 6).
7. Cut into 12 pieces.

One serving contains: *Calories:* **214** *Total Carbohydrate (g):* **31** *Sugar (g):* **13**
Carbohydrate Portions: **3** *Protein (g):* **6** *Total Fat (g):* **9** *Saturated Fat (g):* **1**
Unsaturated Fat (g): **7** *Cholesterol (mg):* **76** *Fibre (g):* **3** *Sodium (mg):* **93** *Salt (g):* **0.2**
Calcium (mg): **68** *Magnesium (mg):* **48** *Iron (mg):* **1.5** *Zinc (mg):* **1** *Glycaemic Load:* **18**

FRUIT TART

Total Time: 2 hrs 50 min (preparation only: 50 min); 10 servings

---

Base: **120 g (4.5 oz) gluten-free oats; 20 g (0.5 oz) gluten-free self-raising flour; 6 tbs almond oil; 1 med egg (or egg replacer); 1 tsp guar gum (or preferred alternative); 1 tbs honey; 28 servings stevia**
Filling: **300 ml (10 fl oz) coconut milk; 4 med eggs; 4 tbs golden flax seed (ground); 3 tbs honey; 3 tbs vanilla extract; 1 serving gelatine or vegetarian gelatine (for 570 ml / 19 oz of liquid); 50 ml (2 fl oz) water; 16 servings stevia**
Decoration: **0.5 med kiwi fruit; 4 strawberries; 10 blackberries (or other berries)**

1. For the base, combine all the ingredients, kneed for a few minutes, form a ball, roll thinly, place in an oven-proof tray, trim, and bake for 15 min (gas mark 6).
2. For the filling, whisk all the ingredients except coconut milk for 1-2 min.
3. Heat up coconut milk to the boiling point, take off the heat and slowly pour in egg mixture stirring, and then heat again stirring continuously for 3-4 min.
4. Take off the heat, add gelatine (diluted in 50 ml of water only) and whisk for 2-3 min (it should start thickening).
5. Pour mixture into the base, decorate with fruit and set in the fridge for 2 hrs.

One serving contains: *Calories:* **329** *Total Carbohydrate (g):* **21** *Sugar (g):* **11**
Carbohydrate Portions: **2.5** *Protein (g):* **9** *Total Fat (g):* **22** *Saturated Fat (g):* **7**
Unsaturated Fat (g): **13** *Cholesterol (mg):* **142** *Fibre (g):* **3** *Sodium (mg):* **62** *Salt (g):* **0.2**
Calcium (mg): **49** *Magnesium (mg):* **59** *Iron (mg):* **3** *Zinc (mg):* **2** *Glycaemic Load:* **14**

FOREST FRUIT CRUMBLE

Total Time: 30-35 min; 6 servings

---

700 g (25 oz) black forest fruit (frozen); 120 g (4.5 oz) gluten-free oats; 120 g (4.5 oz) almonds; 4 tbs coconut cream (or rice cream); 1 tbs honey; 20 servings stevia

1. It is recommended to soak the almonds overnight but this is not essential to the recipe.
2. Defrost black forest fruit overnight.
3. For the crumble topping, mix oats, chopped almonds, cream, honey, and 12 servings of stevia.
4. Mix forest fruit with 8 servings of stevia.
5. Place the fruit in an oven-proof dish and cover with the crumble topping.
6. Bake in a pre-heated oven for 20-25 min, or until golden brown (gas mark 6).
7. Divide into 6 servings.

One serving contains: *Calories:* **270** *Total Carbohydrate (g):* **33** *Sugar (g):* **10** *Carbohydrate Portions:* **2.5** *Protein (g):* **8** *Total Fat (g):* **14** *Saturated Fat (g):* **3** *Unsaturated Fat (g):* **10** *Cholesterol (mg):* **0** *Fibre (g):* **10** *Sodium (mg):* **4** *Salt (g):* **0.01** *Calcium (mg):* **99** *Magnesium (mg):* **108** *Iron (mg):* **3** *Zinc (mg):* **2** *Glycaemic Load:* **13**

LEMON SANDWICH CAKE

Total Time: 55-60 min; 7 servings (1 serving = 1 slice)

Cake: 90 g (3 oz) gluten-free self-raising flour; 50 g (2 oz) cornmeal;
150 g (5.5 oz) plain soya yoghurt; 200 g (7 oz) soft tofu; 3 med eggs (or egg
replacers); 50 ml (2 fl oz) coconut milk; 2 tbs honey; 6 tbs lemon oil extract;
1 tsp gluten-free baking powder; 28 servings stevia; sunflower oil spray
Filling: 80 g (3 oz) dried dates; 3 tbs ground flax seed, 12 tbs water

1. Combine flour, cornmeal, egg yolks, yoghurt, tofu, milk, honey, baking powder, gum, lemon extract and stevia, and stir (or whisk) until the mixture thickens.
2. Beat egg whites (soft peaks) and gently fold into the mixture.
3. Transfer the mixture into a non-stick loaf tin, coated with oil spray (8 sprays) and a dusting of flour, and bake in a pre-heated oven for 25 min (gas mark 6), or until it starts browning.
4. For the filling, blend all the ingredients thoroughly.
5. Allow the cake to cool, cut in half horizontally and apply filling.
6. Cut into 7 slices.

One serving contains: *Calories:* **250** *Total Carbohydrate (g):* **30** *Sugar (g):* **13**
Carbohydrate Portions: **3** *Protein (g):* **8** *Total Fat (g):* **8** *Saturated Fat (g):* **2**
Unsaturated Fat (g): **4** *Cholesterol (mg):* **97** *Fibre (g):* **3** *Sodium (mg):* **147** *Salt (g):* **0.4**
Calcium (mg): **76** *Magnesium (mg):* **52** *Iron (mg):* **1.5** *Zinc (mg):* **1** *Glycaemic Load:* **19**

CHOCOLATE ALMOND CAKE

Total Time: 60 min; 12 servings (1 serving = 1 slice)

Cake: 275 g (9 oz) almonds; 180 g (6.5 oz) gluten-free self-raising flour;
70 g (2.5 oz) sorghum flour (or gluten-free self-raising flour); 4 med eggs
(or egg replacers); 200 ml (7 fl oz) unsweetened almond milk;
4 tbs runny honey; 1 tsp gluten-free baking powder; 1 tsp guar gum
(or preferred alternative); 28 servings stevia; sunflower oil spray
Filling: 120 g (4.5 oz) creamed coconut; 170 g (6 oz) coconut milk;
4 tbs reduced-fat coca powder; 1 tbs honey; 16 servings stevia

1. Grind 250 g of almonds and combine with flour, egg yolks, almond milk, honey, baking powder, gum, stevia, and stir (or whisk) until mixture thickens.
2. Beat egg whites (soft peaks) and fold into the mixture.
3. Transfer mixture into a baking tin, coated with oil spray and a dusting of flour, and bake in a pre-heated oven for 30 min (gas mark 6).
4. Allow cake to cool, cut in half horizontally, apply filling (melt creamed coconut on low heat and blend with the rest of the ingredients; refrigerate for 10-15 min before filling the cake), top with almonds, and cut into 12 slices.

One serving contains: *Calories:* **359** *Total Carbohydrate (g):* **30** *Sugar (g):* **8**
Carbohydrate Portions: **3** *Protein (g):* **10** *Total Fat (g):* **23** *Saturated Fat (g):* **4**
Unsaturated Fat (g): **17** *Cholesterol (mg):* **76** *Fibre (g):* **4** *Sodium (mg):* **82** *Salt (g):* **0.2**
Calcium (mg): **105** *Magnesium (mg):* **98** *Iron (mg):* **2.4** *Zinc (mg):* **2** *Glycaemic Load:* **16**

BLACKCURRANT MOUSSE CAKE

Total Time: 3 hrs 15 min (preparation only: 20 min); 10 servings

---

Base: **120 g (4.5 oz) gluten-free self-raising flour; 2 med eggs (or egg replacers); 100 ml (3.5 fl oz) unsweetened rice milk; 4 tbs almond oil; 2 tbs honey; 16 servings stevia; sunflower oil spray**
Mousse layer: **350 g (12.5 oz) blackcurrants tinned in juice (drained; can use frozen); 200 ml (7 fl oz) unsweetened rice milk; 250 ml (8.5 fl oz) coconut milk; 2 servings gelatine (each for 570 ml / 19 fl oz of liquid); 2 tbs runny honey; 16 servings stevia; 100 ml (3.5 fl oz) water**
Top layer: **blackcurrant jelly (for 570 ml / 19 fl oz of fluid); 470 (16 fl oz) ml water**

1. For the base, combine all the ingredients (whisk or stir) and bake for 20 min (gas mark 6) in a tin coated with oil spray and a dusting of flour.
2. Blend drained blackcurrants with coconut milk, rice milk, honey and stevia, then mix in 2 servings of gelatine (diluted in 100 ml of hot water only).
3. Pour mixture into the baking tray (allow base to cool first) and place in the fridge to set for 1.5 hrs (or freezer for faster result).
4. Top with jelly (diluted in 470 ml of hot water and cooled). Allow to set for 1 hr.

One serving contains: *Calories:* **238** *Total Carbohydrate (g):* **28** *Sugar (g):* **16**
Carbohydrate Portions: **3** *Protein (g):* **6** *Total Fat (g):* **11** *Saturated Fat (g):* **4**
Unsaturated Fat (g): **5** *Cholesterol (mg):* **46** *Fibre (g):* **1** *Sodium (mg):* **37** *Salt (g):* **0.1**
Calcium (mg): **26** *Magnesium (mg):* **26** *Iron (mg):* **1** *Zinc (mg):* **1** *Glycaemic Load:* **17**

HAZELNUT PUDDING
Total Time: 10-15 min; 4 servings

**140 g (5 oz) ground hazelnuts; 25 g (1 oz) chopped hazelnuts;
60 g (2 oz) sultanas; 600 ml (20 oz) unsweetened almond milk
(or hazelnut milk); 2 tbs ground flax seed; 1 tbs honey; 12 servings stevia**

1. Combine almond milk with sultanas, honey and stevia.
2. Cook on low to medium heat until the mixtures starts to bubble, stirring continuously.
3. Take off the heat, add ground hazelnuts and flax seed.
4. Allow to cool down and thicken.
5. Divide into 4 servings and decorate with chopped hazelnuts.

One serving contains: *Calories:* **350** *Total Carbohydrate (g):* **24** *Sugar (g):* **15**
Carbohydrate Portions: **2** *Protein (g):* **8** *Total Fat (g):* **28** *Saturated Fat (g):* **2**
Unsaturated Fat (g): **24** *Cholesterol (mg):* **0** *Fibre (g):* **6** *Sodium (mg):* **3** *Salt (g):* **0.01**
Calcium (mg): **243** *Magnesium (mg):* **92** *Iron (mg):* **2.4** *Zinc (mg):* **1** *Glycaemic Load:* **9**

BEETROOT & LEMON CAKE

Total Time: 60 min; 12 servings (1 serving = 1 slice)

Cake: **200 g (7 oz) gluten-free self-raising flour; 80 g (3 oz) sorghum flour (or gluten-free self-raising flour); 7 med beetroots (cooked in water); 100 ml (3.5 fl oz) coconut milk; 5 med eggs (or egg replacers); 4 tbs runny honey; 1 tsp gluten-free baking powder; 6 tsp allspice; 24 servings stevia; sunflower oil spray**
Filling: **230 g (8 oz) pineapple tinned in juice (drained); 1 med lemon (juiced); 150 g (5.5 oz) creamed coconut; 1 tbs lemon extract**

1. Combine flour, grated beetroot, egg yolks, coconut milk, honey, baking powder, allspice, and stevia (stir or whisk).
2. Beat egg whites (soft peaks) and fold into the mixture.
3. Transfer the mixture into a baking tin, coated with oil spray and a dusting of flour, and bake in a pre-heated oven for 30 min (gas mark 6).
4. Blend pineapple with melted creamed coconut (on low heat) lemon extract and half the lemon juice, and refrigerate for 10-15 min.
5. When cool, slice cake in half, drizzle remaining lemon juice onto base, and fill.

One serving contains: *Calories:* **285** *Total Carbohydrate (g):* **34** *Sugar (g):* **13**
Carbohydrate Portions: **3.5** *Protein (g):* **7** *Total Fat (g):* **14** *Saturated Fat (g):* **3**
Unsaturated Fat (g): **9** *Cholesterol (mg):* **94** *Fibre (g):* **3** *Sodium (mg):* **124** *Salt (g):* **0.3**
Calcium (mg): **45** *Magnesium (mg):* **45** *Iron (mg):* **2** *Zinc (mg):* **1** *Glycaemic Load:* **17**

COCONUT & RASPBERRY CAKE

Total Time: 40-45 min; 12 servings (1 serving = 1 piece)

---

300 g (11 oz) unsweetened desiccated coconut; 50 g (2 oz) gluten-free self-raising flour; 50 g (2 oz) sorghum flour (or gluten-free self-raising flour); 170 g (6 oz) raspberries (fresh or frozen); 4 med eggs (or egg replacers); 150 ml (5 fl oz) unsweetened almond milk; 150 ml (5 fl oz) coconut milk; 4 tbs runny honey; 1 tsp gluten-free baking powder; 24 servings stevia; sunflower oil spray

1. Combine coconut, flour, egg yolks, almond milk, coconut milk, honey, baking powder and stevia (stir or whisk).
2. Beat egg whites (soft peaks) and gently fold into the mixture.
3. Coat a non-stick baking tin with oil spray (8 sprays) and a dusting of flour.
4. Transfer the mixture into the baking tray and decorate with raspberries (gently push them in).
5. Bake in a pre-heated oven for 30 min (gas mark 6).
6. Cut into 12 pieces.

One serving contains: *Calories:* **276** *Total Carbohydrate (g):* **20** *Sugar (g):* **8** *Carbohydrate Portions:* **2** *Protein (g):* **5** *Total Fat (g):* **21** *Saturated Fat (g):* **17** *Unsaturated Fat (g):* **2** *Cholesterol (mg):* **76** *Fibre (g):* **5** *Sodium (mg):* **91** *Salt (g):* **0.2** *Calcium (mg):* **45** *Magnesium (mg):* **40** *Iron (mg):* **2** *Zinc (mg):* **1** *Glycaemic Load:* **9**

VERY PEARY YOGHURT CAKE

Total Time: 45 min; 10 servings (1 serving = 1 slice)

---

5 med ripe pears; 6 small dried figs; 500 g (18 oz) plain soya yoghurt; 130 g (4.5 oz) gluten-free self-raising flour; 4 med eggs (or egg replacers); 4 tbs runny honey; 3 tbs vanilla extract; 1 tsp guar gum (or preferred alternative); 40 servings stevia; sunflower oil spray

1. Combine flour, yoghurt, egg yolks, honey, gum, baking powder, vanilla extract and stevia, and stir (or whisk) until the mixture thickens.
2. Beat egg whites (soft peaks).
3. Gently fold egg whites and diced pears into the mixture.
4. Coat a non-stick baking tin with oil spray (8 sprays) and a dusting of flour.
5. Transfer the mixture into the tin, smooth it out, and decorate with fig slices.
6. Bake in a pre-heated oven for 30 min (gas mark 6).
7. Cut into 10 slices.

One serving contains: *Calories:* **184** *Total Carbohydrate (g):* **30** *Sugar (g):* **20** *Carbohydrate Portions:* **3** *Protein (g):* **6** *Total Fat (g):* **4** *Saturated Fat (g):* **1** *Unsaturated Fat (g):* **2** *Cholesterol (mg):* **91** *Fibre (g):* **3** *Sodium (mg):* **107** *Salt (g):* **0.2** *Calcium (mg):* **107** *Magnesium (mg):* **26** *Iron (mg):* **1** *Zinc (mg):* **1** *Glycaemic Load:* **18**

CASHEW & APRICOT CAKE

Total Time: 45 min; 12 servings (1 serving = 1 piece)

---

250 g (9 oz) cashew nuts; 250 g (9 oz) dried apricots; 100 g (3.5 oz) gluten-free self-raising flour; 70 g (2.5 oz) gluten-free oats; 4 med eggs (or egg replacers); 3 tbs runny honey; 200 ml (7 fl oz) unsweetened almond milk; 1 tsp gluten-free baking powder; 28 servings stevia; sunflower oil spray

1. Cashew nuts should be preferably soaked overnight but this is not essential to the recipe (do not soak if bought ground).
2. Grind nuts and combine with flour, oats, egg yolks, almond milk, honey, baking powder, and stevia (stir or whisk).
3. Beat egg whites (soft peaks).
4. Gently fold egg whites and chopped apricots into the mixture.
5. Transfer the mixture into a non-stick baking tin, coated with oil spray (8 sprays) and a dusting of flour.
6. Bake in a pre-heated oven for 30 min (gas mark 6).
7. Cut into 12 pieces.

One serving contains: *Calories:* **249** *Total Carbohydrate (g):* **29** *Sugar (g):* **13** *Carbohydrate Portions:* **3** *Protein (g):* **8** *Total Fat (g):* **12** *Saturated Fat (g):* **2** *Unsaturated Fat (g):* **8** *Cholesterol (mg):* **76** *Fibre (g):* **3** *Sodium (mg):* **83** *Salt (g):* **0.2** *Calcium (mg):* **63** *Magnesium (mg):* **87** *Iron (mg):* **3** *Zinc (mg):* **2** *Glycaemic Load:* **18**

NUTTY CHOCOLATE MOUSSE

Total Time: 10-15 min; 4 servings

---

4 ripe med bananas; 300 ml (10 fl oz) unsweetened almond milk (or rice milk); 70 g (2.5 oz) ground Brazil nuts; 40 g (1.5 oz) chopped pecan nuts; 2 tbs ground flax seed; 4 tbs reduced-fat cocoa powder; 5-6 servings stevia

1. Blend mashed bananas (you may want to leave some for decoration) with almond milk, ground Brazil nuts, flax seed, cocoa powder, and stevia.
2. Divide into 4 servings and decorate with chopped pecan nuts and small pieces of banana.

One serving contains: *Calories:* **321** *Total Carbohydrate (g):* **31** *Sugar (g):* **13** *Carbohydrate Portions:* **2.5** *Protein (g):* **7** *Total Fat (g):* **23** *Saturated Fat (g):* **4** *Unsaturated Fat (g):* **17** *Cholesterol (mg):* **0** *Fibre (g):* **9** *Sodium (mg):* **4** *Salt (g):* **0.01** *Calcium (mg):* **149** *Magnesium (mg):* **154** *Iron (mg):* **2** *Zinc (mg):* **2** *Glycaemic Load:* **8**

RHUBARB & RAISIN ROULADE

Total Time: 45-50 min; 6 servings (1 serving = 1 slice)

Roulade: 300 g (11 oz) plain soya yoghurt; 3 med eggs (or egg replacers);
7 tbs gluten-free self-raising flour; 1 tsp guar gum (or preferred alternative);
12 servings stevia
Filling: 150 g (5.5 oz) rhubarb; 1 large orange; 80 g (3 oz) raisins (or sultanas);
30 ml (1 fl oz) orange juice; 1 tbs honey; 12 portions stevia

1. For the filling, combine chopped rhubarb and orange with the other ingredients, and cook for 20-25 min on low heat, stirring occasionally.
2. For the roulade, combine yoghurt, flour, egg yolks, gum and stevia, and stir (or whisk) until the mixture thickens.
3. Beat egg whites (soft peaks) and gently fold into the mixture.
4. Spread mixture thinly onto parchment paper, place on a flat tray (approx. 25 x 35 cm), and bake in a pre-heated oven for 20 min (gas mark 6).
5. Allow to cool, peel off paper (with paper facing up), transfer back onto paper, spread filling all over, roll slowly (using paper to help), and cut into 6 slices.

One serving contains: *Calories:* **173** *Total Carbohydrate (g):* **26** *Sugar (g):* **15**
Carbohydrate Portions: **2.5** *Protein (g):* **7** *Total Fat (g):* **5** *Saturated Fat (g):* **1**
Unsaturated Fat (g): **2** *Cholesterol (mg):* **113** *Fibre (g):* **2** *Sodium (mg):* **96** *Salt (g):* **0.2**
Calcium (mg): **124** *Magnesium (mg):* **23** *Iron (mg):* **1** *Zinc (mg):* **1** *Glycaemic Load:* **17**

    Ca

SPICED APPLE CAKE

Total Time: 45 min; 12 servings (1 serving = 1 slice)

---

10 med apples; 2 ripe med bananas; 170 g (6 oz) gluten-free self-raising flour;
50 g (2 oz) sorghum flour (or gluten-free self-raising flour); 4 med eggs
(or egg replacers); 3 tbs runny honey; 6 tsp ground cinnamon; 3 tsp of ground
cloves; 1 tsp gluten-free baking powder; 30 servings stevia; sunflower oil spray

1. Combine flour, grated apples (drain most of the juice), mashed bananas, egg yolks, honey, spices, baking powder, and stevia (stir or whisk).
2. Beat egg whites (soft peaks) and gently fold into the mixture.
3. Transfer the mixture into a non-stick baking tin, coated with oil spray (8 sprays) and a dusting of flour.
4. Bake in a pre-heated oven for 30 min (gas mark 6).
5. Cut into 12 slices.

One serving contains: *Calories:* **162** *Total Carbohydrate (g):* **32** *Sugar (g):* **11**
Carbohydrate Portions: **3** *Protein (g):* **4** *Total Fat (g):* **3** *Saturated Fat (g):* **1**
Unsaturated Fat (g): **2** *Cholesterol (mg):* **76** *Fibre (g):* **3** *Sodium (mg):* **80** *Salt (g):* **0.2**
Calcium (mg): **62** *Magnesium (mg):* **26** *Iron (mg):* **1** *Zinc (mg):* **1** *Glycaemic Load:* **16**

SUMMER FRUIT & PEACH JELLY

Total Time: 2 hrs 50 min (preparation only: 20 min); 12 servings

---

400 g (14 oz) summer fruit (frozen); 400 g (14 oz) peaches tinned in juice; 800 ml (27 fl oz) unsweetened rice milk; 4 servings gelatine or vegetarian gelatine (each for 570 ml / 19 fl oz of liquid); 16 servings stevia; 280 ml (9.5 fl oz) water

1. Defrost summer fruit (this can be done overnight).
2. Blend summer fruit, mix with 4 servings of stevia and 1 serving of gelatine (diluted in only 70 ml of hot water), pour into a tray (or flat dish) and place in the fridge to set for 1.5 hrs (or freezer for faster result).
3. Repeat the same process with peaches (blend with juice).
4. After the summer fruit and peach jelly are set, cut into small chunks and transfer into a bigger dish.
5. Dilute 2 servings of gelatine in 140 ml of hot water, mix with rice milk and 8 servings of stevia, allow the mixture to cool, then slowly pour over the fruit jelly chunks and leave in the fridge to set for at least 1 hr.
6. Cut into 12 pieces.

One serving contains: *Calories:* **75** *Total Carbohydrate (g):* **14** *Sugar (g):* **5** *Carbohydrate Portions:* **1.5** *Protein (g):* **4** *Total Fat (g):* **1** *Saturated Fat (g):* **0** *Unsaturated Fat (g):* **0** *Cholesterol (mg):* **1** *Fibre (g):* **2** *Sodium (mg):* **32** *Salt (g):* **0.08** *Calcium (mg):* **19** *Magnesium (mg):* **10** *Iron (mg):* **0** *Zinc (mg):* **0** *Glycaemic Load:* **4**

EXTRAS

EGGLESS MAYONNAISE

Total Time: 8-10 min; 16 tablespoons

---

7 tbs oil (sunflower, almond, avocado or other); 2 tbs apple cider vinegar; 80 ml (2.5 fl oz) unsweetened almond milk; 3 tbs golden flax seed (ground); 0.5 tbs runny honey; 0.25 tsp sea salt

1. Mix all the ingredients together except for oil.
2. Blend on low setting for 30-60 seconds, using immersion blender, then slowly start adding oil and continue to blend until the mixture thickens.
3. Store in the fridge.

* you can customise this recipe by adding e.g. onion granules, garlic powder, mustard, horseradish sauce, or any of your favourite spices

One tablespoon contains: *Calories:* **95** *Total Carbohydrate (g):* **1.5** *Sugar (g):* **1** *Carbohydrate Portions:* **0** *Protein (g):* **0.5** *Total Fat (g):* **10** *Saturated Fat (g):* **1.5** *Unsaturated Fat (g):* **8.5** *Cholesterol (mg):* **0** *Fibre (g):* **0.5** *Sodium (mg):* **60** *Salt (g):* **0.1** *Calcium (mg):* **15** *Magnesium (mg):* **9** *Iron (mg):* **0** *Zinc (mg):* **0** *Glycaemic Load:* **0.5**

WHITE SAUCE

Total Time: 10-15 min; 4 servings

---

100 ml (3.5 fl oz) coconut milk; 200 ml (7 fl oz) unsweetened almond milk; 1 tsp guar gum (or preferred alternative); salt and pepper (to taste)

1. Combine coconut milk with almond milk and a pinch of salt and pepper, and cook on low to medium heat.
2. Add guar gum while stirring (ideally use a sieve to prevent sauce from going lumpy).
3. Continue to cook, stirring continuously, until the mixture reaches the required thickness (it will get thicker as it cools down).
4. If the sauce is lumpy at this stage, use a whisk to make it smooth.
5. Add more salt and pepper if required.

* for something a bit different, add some onion granules, garlic powder and (or) your favourite herbs

One serving contains: *Calories:* **50** *Total Carbohydrate (g):* **1** *Sugar (g):* **1**
Carbohydrate Portions: **0** *Protein (g):* **1** *Total Fat (g):* **5** *Saturated Fat (g):* **3**
Unsaturated Fat (g): **1** *Cholesterol (mg):* **0** *Fibre (g):* **0.3** *Sodium (mg):* **3** *Salt (g):* **0.01**
Calcium (mg): **64** *Magnesium (mg):* **12** *Iron (mg):* **1** *Zinc (mg):* **0** *Glycaemic Load:* **1**

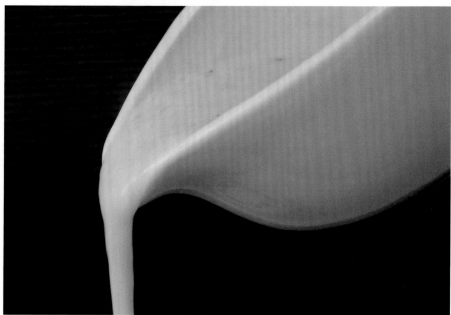

DUMPLINGS

Total Time: 30-35 min; 4 servings

1.5 small potatoes (approx. 110 g); 50 g (2 oz) gluten-free flour; 1 small egg (or egg replacer); 1 tsp guar gum (or preferred alternative); 0.25 tsp sea salt

1. Cook diced potatoes for 15 min on medium heat, drain and mash.
2. Combine mashed potato with the rest of the ingredients and knead for a few minutes.
3. Form the dough into a thin tube of 1.5-2 cm diameter and cut into small chunks (as shown in the picture).
4. Put in boiling water and cook for 2-3 min on medium heat (wait for the dumplings to rise to the surface).
5. Drain and serve with soups or sauces.

One serving contains: *Calories:* **82** *Total Carbohydrate (g):* **14** *Sugar (g):* **0**
Carbohydrate Portions: **1.5** *Protein (g):* **9** *Total Fat (g):* **2** *Saturated Fat (g):* **0**
Unsaturated Fat (g): **1** *Cholesterol (mg):* **49** *Fibre (g):* **1** *Sodium (mg):* **167** *Salt (g):* **0.4**
Calcium (mg): **14** *Magnesium (mg):* **16** *Iron (mg):* **1** *Zinc (mg):* **0** *Glycaemic Load:* **9**

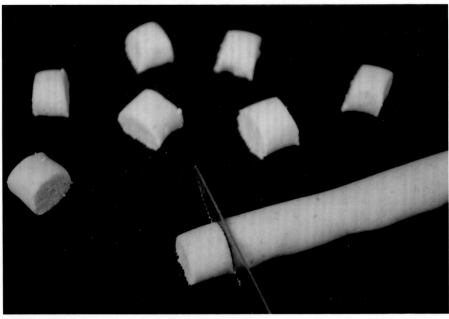

BASIL DRESSING

Total Time: 5-8 min; 4 servings

---

200 ml (7 fl oz) coconut milk; 25 g (1 oz) fresh basil; 0.5 med lemon (juiced); 1 clove garlic (peeled); 2 tbs balsamic vinegar; salt and pepper (to taste)

1. Blend coconut milk, basil, lemon juice, crushed garlic and vinegar until smooth.
2. Add salt and pepper to taste.

* use as salad dressing or with meat and fish dishes

One tablespoon contains: *Calories:* **92** *Total Carbohydrate (g):* **3** *Sugar (g):* **1** *Carbohydrate Portions:* **0.5** *Protein (g):* **1** *Total Fat (g):* **9** *Saturated Fat (g):* **7** *Unsaturated Fat (g):* **1** *Cholesterol (mg):* **0** *Fibre (g):* **0** *Sodium (mg):* **7** *Salt (g):* **0.02** *Calcium (mg):* **18** *Magnesium (mg):* **23** *Iron (mg):* **2** *Zinc (mg):* **0** *Glycaemic Load:* **1**

CURRIED MEATBALLS

Total Time: 20-25 min; 4 servings

---

200 g (7 oz) extra-lean beef mince; 1 tsp cumin powder; 1 tsp allspice; 1 tsp dried coriander; 1 tsp ginger powder; 0.5 turmeric; 4 tbs gluten-free flour (plain); 1 tsp sea salt; 0.5 tbs coconut oil

1. Combine beef, flour and spices, and knead for a couple of minutes.
2. Form into balls (16 bigger ones or 20 smaller ones).
3. Heat coconut oil in a frying pan.
4. Place the meatballs in the pan and cook for 10-12 min on medium heat, turning them regularly to prevent burning.
5. Serve with soups or sauces.

One serving contains: *Calories:* **120** *Total Carbohydrate (g):* **9** *Sugar (g):* **0**
Carbohydrate Portions: **1** *Protein (g):* **12** *Total Fat (g):* **4** *Saturated Fat (g):* **1**
Unsaturated Fat (g): **3** *Cholesterol (mg):* **29** *Fibre (g):* **1** *Sodium (mg):* **624** *Salt (g):* **1.6**
Calcium (mg): **24** *Magnesium (mg):* **26** *Iron (mg):* **2.5** *Zinc (mg):* **2** *Glycaemic Load:* **6**

QUICK WHEAT, GLUTEN AND DAIRY-FREE SNACK IDEAS

* Note that the snack ideas are arranged by estimated glycaemic load per serving (in ascending order)

Snack	Calories per serving	Total Carbohydrate per serving (g)	Carbohydrate Portions per serving	Total Fat per serving (g)	Estimated Glycaemic Load per serving
TOMATO SARDINES LETTUCE WRAP Mix 1 tin of sardines in tomato sauce with 2 chopped spring onions, and salt and pepper (to taste). Wrap in 2 med iceberg lettuce leaves.	163	3	0.5	10	1
CHICKEN WITH AVOCADO DIP Serve 100 g (3.5 oz) of chicken breast slices with 1 serving of avocado dip (recipe on p. 85).	266	7	1	14	2
CUCUMBER & CELERY STICKS WITH OLIVE DIP Cut a third of large cucumber and 2 med celery stalks into sticks, and serve with 100 g (3.5 oz) of black pitted olives (blended with 1tbs of olive oil, 1 tbs of balsamic vinegar and seasoning).	249	11	1	23	3
CARROT STICKS WITH PECAN COCONUT DIP Cut 1 large carrot into sticks and serve with 30 g (1 oz) of ground pecan nuts blended with 2 tbs of coconut milk.	297	16	1.5	25	4

Snack	Calories per serving	Total Carbohydrate per serving (g)	Carbohydrate Portions per serving	Total Fat per serving (g)	Estimated Glycaemic Load per serving
APPLE WEDGES WITH CASHEW BUTTER Cut 1 med apple into wedges and spread with cashew butter (2 tbs). To make your own cashew butter, roast 30 g (1 oz) of cashew nuts in the oven for 10 min and blend with 2 tbs of water until smooth.	236	26	2.5	14	7
MIXED BERRY YOGHURT Blend 150 g (5.5 oz) of plain soya yoghurt with 150 g (5.5 oz) of mixed berries (fresh or frozen). Add stevia to taste.	140	18	1.5	4	9
FROZEN BANANA WITH CHOCOLATE DIP Slice 1 med banana and freeze partially. Serve with 4 tbs of coconut cream blended with 1 tbs of reduced-fat cocoa powder and stevia (to taste).	219	27	2.5	13	9
ASSORTED PEPPER STRIPS WITH HUMMUS Cut 0.5 of red pepper and 0.5 of yellow pepper into strips. Serve with 8 tbs of hummus (recipe on p. 68).	201	24	2	9	10
WALNUT & APRICOT MIX Mix 14 walnut halves with 7 apricots.	261	22	2	19	15
OATCAKES WITH HAM & CUCUMBER Top gluten-free oatcakes (x 4) with ham (4 slices) and cucumber (12 slices).	284	26	1.5	10	15

Snack	Calories per serving	Total Carbohydrate per serving (g)	Carbohydrate Portions per serving	Total Fat per serving (g)	Estimated Glycaemic Load per serving
CHOCO-YOGHURT WITH FIGS Blend 150 g (5.5 oz) of plain soya yoghurt with 2 tbs of fat-reduced cocoa powder and 5 servings of stevia (or to taste). Add 2 small dried figs (chopped).	192	31	2.5	6	16
RICE CAKES WITH SMOKED SALMON & EGGLESS MAYO Top rice cakes (x 3) with eggless mayo (3 tbs; recipe on p. 174), smoked salmon slices (60 g; 2 oz), and drizzle of lemon juice.	277	23	2.5	13	16
RICE CAKES WITH CHOCOLATE ALMOND BUTTER Top rice cakes (x 3) with a blend of almond butter (2 tbs) and reduced-fat cocoa powder (1 tbs) and stevia (to taste) To make your own almond butter, roast 30 g (1 oz) of almonds in the oven for 10 min and blend with 2 tbs of water until smooth.	334	41	3.5	19	16
TORTILLA CHIPS WITH AVOCADO SALSA Slice 30 g (1 oz) of oven-baked tortilla chips with 1 serving of avocado salsa (recipe on p. 66).	237	30	2.5	12	17
CORN CAKES WITH PUMPKIN SEED BUTTER Spread 2 tbs of pumpkin seed butter on corn cakes (x 3).	281	29	3	15	17

Snack	Calories per serving	Total Carbohydrate per serving (g)	Carbohydrate Portions per serving	Total Fat per serving (g)	Estimated Glycaemic Load per serving
OATCAKES WITH SUN-DRIED TOMATO SPREAD Top gluten-free oatcakes (x 4) with a blend of sun-dried tomatoes [soak 25 g (1 oz) of sun-dried tomatoes in hot water for 10-15 min, then drain], 1 tbs of mixed dried herbs, 1 tbs of olive oil, and pepper (to taste).	323	32	3	19	17
RICE CAKES WITH PEACH PUREÉ Top rice cakes (x 3) with peach pureé (blend 0.3 of a tin of peaches tinned in juice; drain first).	139	30	3	1	18
COCONUT & CINNAMON CORN CAKES Mix 3 tbs of coconut milk with 1 tsp of ground cinnamon and spread on corn cakes (x 3).	194	27	2.5	8	18
OATCAKES WITH HUMMUS Top gluten-free oatcakes (x 4) with hummus (4 tbs; recipe on p. 68).	245	31	3	11	18
COCONUT RICE PUFFS Mix 25 g (1 oz) of brown puffed rice with 25 g (1 oz) of unsweetened desiccated coconut and 1 tsp of ground cinnamon. Add 150 ml (3.5 fl oz) of unsweetened rice milk, and stevia to taste.	339	42	4	18	18

References

Adebamowo, CA *et al.* (2008) Milk consumption and acne in teenaged boys. *J Am Acad Dermatol*, 58:787-793.

Albert, BB *et al.* (2013) Oxidation of Marine Omega-3 Supplements and Human Health. *Biomed Res Int*, 2013:464921.

Arcidiacono, B *et al.* (2012) Insulin resistance and cancer risk: an overview of the pathogenetic mechanisms. *Exp Diabetes Res*, 2012:789174.

Assunção, ML *et al.* (2009) Effects of dietary coconut oil on the biochemical and anthropometric profiles of women presenting abdominal obesity. *Lipids*, 44(7):593-601.

Arunima, S & Rajamohan T (2012) Virgin coconut oil improves hepatic lipid metabolism in rats-compared with copra oil, olive oil and sunflower oil. *Indian J Exp Biol*, 50(11):802-9.

Baars, AJ *et al.* (2004) Dioxins, dioxin-like PCBs and non-dioxin-like PCBs in foodstuffs: occurrence and dietary intake in the Netherlands. *Toxicol Lett*, 151:51-61.

Biesiekierski, JR *et al.* (2011) Gluten causes gastrointestinal symptoms in subjects without celiac disease: a double-blind randomized placebo-controlled trial. *American J Gastroenterol*, 106(3):508-14.

Bischoff-Ferrari, HA *et al.* (2007) Calcium intake and hip fracture risk in men and women: a meta-analysis of prospective cohort studies and randomized controlled trials. *Am J Clin Nutr*, 86:1780-90.

Block, RJ & Bolling, D. (1946) The amino acid composition of cow and human milk proteins. *Arch Biochem*, 10:359-63.

Brottveit, M *et al.* (2013) Mucosal cytokine response after short-term gluten challenge in celiac disease and non-celiac gluten sensitivity. *Am J Gastroenterol,* 108(5):842-50.

Brusick, DJ (2008) A critical review of the genetic toxicity of steviol and steviol glycosides. *Food Chem Toxicol*, 46 Suppl 7:S83-91.

Carr, AC (2012) Depressed mood associated with gluten sensitivity-resolution of symptoms with a gluten-free diet. *N Z Med J*, 23;125(1366):81-2.

Carroccio, A *et al.* (2012) Non-celiac wheat sensitivity diagnosed by double-blind placebo-controlled challenge: exploring a new clinical entity. *Am J Gastroenterol*, 107(12):1898-906.

Chafen, JJ *et al.* (2010) Diagnosing and managing common food allergies: a systematic review. *JAMA*, 12;303(18):1848-56.

Chan, P *et al.* (2000) A double-blind placebo-controlled study of the effectiveness and tolerability of oral stevioside in human hypertension. *Br J Clin Pharmacol*, 50:215-20.

Chiu, CJ *et al.* (2011). Informing food choices and health outcomes by use of the dietary glycemic index. *Nutr Rev,* 69 (4): 231-42.

Cramer, DW *et al.* (2000) A case-control study of galactose consumption and metabolism in relation to ovarian cancer. *Cancer Epidemiol Biomarkers Prev*, 9:95-101.

Curi, R *et al.* (1986) Effect of Stevia rebaudiana on glucose tolerance in normal adult humans. *Braz J Med Biol Res*, 19:771-4.

Dalla Pellegrina, C *et al.* (2009) Effects of wheat germ agglutinin on human gastrointestinal epithelium: insights from an experimental model of immune/epithelial cell interaction. *Toxicol Appl Pharmacol*, 1;237(2):146-53.

Dalla Pellegrina, C. *et al.* (1986) Studies on the joint cytotoxicity of Wheat Germ Agglutinin and monensin. *Brain Res*, 393(2):169-75.

Denton, C (2012) The elimination/challenge diet. *Minn Med*, 95(12):43-4.

Department of Health (1991) *Dietary Reference Values for Food and Energy and Nutrients for the United Kingdom.Report of the Panel on Dietary Reference Values of the Committee on Medical Aspects of Food Policy.* Norwich: The Stationery Office.

Di Berardino, F *et al.* (2013) Ménière disease and gluten sensitivity: recovery after a gluten-free diet. *Am J Otolaryngol,_*34(4):355-6.

Dickerson, F *et al.* (2012) Markers of gluten sensitivity in acute mania: A longitudinal study. *Psychiatry Res*, 196(1):68-71.

Dickey, W (2008) Making oats safer for patients with coeliac disease. *Eur J Gastroenterol Hepatol*, 20(6):494-5.

Du Toit, G *et al.* (2010) Identifying and managing cow's milk protein allergy. *Arch Dis Child Educ Pract Ed*, 95(5):134-44.

Ebbeling, CB *et al.* (2003) A reduced-glycemic load diet in the treatment of adolescent obesity. *Arch Pediatr Adolesc Med*, 157(8):773-9.

Egger, J *et al.* (1983) Is migraine food allergy? A double-blind controlled trial of oligoantigenic diet treatment. *Lancet,* 2:865-869.

Faber, MT *et al.* (2012) Use of dairy products, lactose, and calcium and risk of ovarian cancer - results from a Danish case-control study. *Acta Oncol,* 51:454-464.

Fälth-Magnusson, K & Magnusson, KE (1995) Elevated levels of serum antibodies to the lectin wheat germ agglutinin in celiac children lend support to the gluten-lectin theory of celiac disease. *Pediatr Allergy Immunol*, 6(2):98-102.

Farlow, DW *et al.* (2009) Quantitative measurement of endogenous estrogen metabolites, risk-factors for development of breast cancer, in commercial milk products by LC-MS/MS. *J Chromatogr B Analyt Technol Biomed Life Sci,* 877:1327-1334.

Fasano, A *et al.* (2011) Divergence of gut permeability and mucosal immune gene expression in two gluten-associated conditions: celiac disease and gluten sensitivity. *BMC Med*, 9;9:23.

Fasano, A *et al.* (2012) Spectrum of gluten-related disorders: consensus on new nomenclature and classification. *BMC Med*, 7;10:13.

Feskanich, D *et al.* (2003) Calcium, vitamin D, milk consumption, and hip fractures: a prospective study among postmenopausal women. *Am J Clin Nutr*, 77(2):504-11.

Feskanich, D *et al.* (1997) Milk, dietary calcium, and bone fractures in women: a 12-year prospective study. *Am J Public Health*, 87(6):992-7.

Food Standards Agency (2002) *Food portion sizes* (3rd ed). Norwich: The Stationery Office.

Foods Standards Agency (2002) *McCance and Widdowson's the composition of foods* (6th ed). Cambridge: Royal Society of Chemistry.

Foster-Powell, K *et al.* (2002) International table of glycemic index and glycemic load values: 2002. *Am J Clin Nutr*, 76(1):5-56.

Garrow, JS *et al.* (2001) *Human nutrition and dietetics* (10th ed). London: Harcourt Publishers.

Gibney, M. *et al.* (2004) *Public Health Nutrition. The Nutrition Society Textbook.* Oxford: Blackwell Publishing.

Gonzalez, CA & Riboli, E (2010) Diet and cancer prevention: Contributions from the European Prospective Investigation into Cancer and Nutrition (EPIC) study. *Eur J Cancer*, 46:2555-2562.

Gregersen, S *et al.* (2004) Atihyperglycemic effects of stevioside in type 2 diabetic subjects. *Metabolism*, 53:73-6.

Gunter, MJ *et al.* (2009) Insulin, insulin-like growth factor-I, and risk of breast cancer in post-menopausal women. *J Natl Cancer Inst*, 101(1):48-60.

Gyawu, P & Pope, GS (1983) Oestrogens in milk. J Steroid Biochem,19(1C):877-82.

Hadjivassiliou, M *et al.* (2002) Gluten sensitivity as a neurological illness. *J Neurol Neurosurg Psychiatry*, 72(5):560-3.

Harvard School of Public Health. Calcium and Milk: What's Best for Your Bones and Health? (http://www.hsph.harvard.edu/nutritionsource/calcium-full-story. Accessed on 23 May 2013)

Hosseinpour-Niazi, S *et al.* (2013) Dietary glycemic index, glycemic load, and cardiovascular disease risk factors: Tehran Lipid and Glucose Study. *Arch Iran Med*, 16(7):401-7.

Huang, CB *et al.* (2011) Short- and medium-chain fatty acids exhibit antimicrobial activity for oral microorganisms. *Arch Oral Biol*, 56(7):650-4.

Hu, J. *et al.* (2013) Glycemic index, glycemic load and cancer risk. *Ann Oncol*, 24(1):245-51.

Ismail, NH *et al.* (2012) High glycemic load diet, milk and ice cream consumption are related to acne vulgaris in Malaysian young adults: a case control study. *BMC Dermatol*, 16;12:13.

Ji, S (2008) The dark side of wheat – new perspectives on celiac disease & wheat intolerance. *Journal of Gluten Sensitivity*, Santa Rosa: www.celiac.com (http://www.greenmedinfo.com/page/dark-side-wheat-new-perspectives-celiac-disease-wheat-intolerance-sayer-ji.Accessed on 30 May 2013).

Ji, S Opening Pandora's bread box: the critical role of wheat lectin in human disease (http://www.greenmedinfo.com/page/opening-pandoras-bread-box-critical-role-wheat-lectin-human-disease. Accessed on 30 May 2013).

Larsson, SC *et al.* (2004) Milk and lactose intakes and ovarian cancer risk in the Swedish Mammography Cohort. *Am J Clin Nutr,* 80:1353-1357.

Lebren, M & Rendu, F (1986) Further characterization of wheat germ agglutinin interaction with human platelets: exposure of fibrinogen receptors. *Thromb Haemost*, 15;56(3):323-7.

Luopajärvi, K *et al.* (2008) Enhanced levels of cow's milk antibodies in infancy in children who develop type 1 diabetes later in childhood. *Pediatr Diabetes*, 9(5):434-41.

Kang, JX (2005) Balance of omega-6/omega-3 essential fatty acids is important for health. The evidence from gene transfer studies. World Rev Nutr Diet., 95:93-102.

Karlsson, A (1999) Wheat germ agglutinin induces NADPH-oxidase activity in human neutrophils by interaction with mobilizable receptors. *Infect Immun*, 67(7):3461-8.

Key, TJ *et al.* (2010) Insulin-like growth factor 1 (IGF1), IGF binding protein 3 (IGFBP3), and breast cancer risk: pooled individual data analysis of 17 prospective studies. *Lancet Oncol*, 11(6):530-42.

Kulkarni, K (2003) *Carbohydrate counting for pump therapy: insulin to carbohydrate ratios. In A Core Curriculum for Diabetes Education. Diabetes Management Therapies* (5th ed). Chicago American Association of Diabetes Educators.

Kurek. M *et al.* (1992). A naturally occurring opioid peptide from cow's milk, beta-casomorphine -7, is a direct histamine releaser in man. *Int Arch Allergy Immunol,* 97 (2): 115-120.

185

Lin, P *et al.* (2001) The DASH diet and sodium reduction improve markers of bone turnover and calcium metabolism in adults. *J Nutr,* 133:3130-3136.

Lee, AR *et al.* (2009) The effect of substituting alternative grains in the diet on the nutritional profile of the gluten-free diet. *J Hum Nutr Diet,* 22(4):359-63.

Lloyd, T *et al.* (2002) Modifiable determinants of bone status in young women. *Bone,* 30:416-421.

Mansfield, LE *et al.* (1985) Food allergy and adult migraine; double-blind and mediator confirmation of an allergic etiology. *Ann Allergy,* 55:126-129.

Marina, AM *et al.* (2009) Antioxidant capacity and phenolic acids of virgin coconut oil. *Int J Food Sci Nutr,* 60 Suppl 2:114-23.

Marsh, K. *et al.* (2011) Glycemic index and glycemic load of carbohydrates in the diabetes diet. *Curr Diab Rep,* 11(2):120-7.

Melnik, B (2009) Milk consumption: aggravating factor of acne and promoter of chronic diseases of Western societies. *J Dtsch Dermatol Ges,* 7(4):364-70.

Melnik, BC & Schmitz, G (2009) Role of insulin, insulin-like growth factor-1, hyperglycaemic food and milk consumption in the pathogenesis of acne vulgaris. *Exp Dermatol,* 18(10):833-41.

Mishkind, M *et al.* (1980) Distribution of wheat germ agglutinin in young wheat plants. *Plant Physiol,* Nov;66(5):950-5.

Nachbar, MS & Oppenheim, JD (1980) Lectins in the United States diet: a survey of lectins in commonly consumed foods and a review of the literature. *Am J Clin Nutr,* 33(11):2338-45.

Nevin, KG & Rajamohan, T (2004) Beneficial effects of virgin coconut oil on lipid parameters and in vitro LDL oxidation. *Clin Biochem,* 37(9):830-5.

Outwater, JL *et al.* (1997) Dairy products and breast cancer: the IGF-1, estrogen, and bGH hypothesis. *Med Hypothesis,* 48:453-461.

Owusu, W *et al.* (1997) Calcium intake and the incidence of forearm and hip fractures among men. *J Nutr,* 127:1782-87.

Park, HM *et al.* (2011) Calcium from plant sources is beneficial to lowering the risk of osteoporosis in postmenopausal Korean women. *Nutr Res,* 31(1):27-32.

Pizzorno, L & Ferril, W (2005) Chapter 32: Clinical approaches to hormonal and neuroendocrine imbalances. Thyroid. In *Textbook of functional medicine.* Gig Harbor, WA: Institute for Functional Medicine.

Price. AJ *et al.* (2012) Insulin-like growth factor-I concentration and risk of prostate cancer: results from the European Prospective Investigation into Cancer and Nutrition. *Cancer Epidemiol Biomarkers Prev,* 21(9):1531-41.

Pusztai, A & Grant, G (1998) Assessment of lectin inactivation by heat and digestion. *Methods Mol Med,* 9:505-14.

Pusztai, A *et al.* (1993) Antinutritive effects of wheat-germ agglutinin and other N-acetylglucosamine-specific lectins. *Br J Nutr,* 70(1):313-21.

Romieu, I *et al.* (2012) Dietary glycemic index and glycemic load and breast cancer risk in the European Prospective Investigation into Cancer and Nutrition (EPIC). *Am J Clin Nutr,* 96 (2):345-55.

Rostami, K & Hogg-Kollars, S (2012) A Patient's Journey. Non-coeliac gluten sensitivity. *BMJ,* 30;345:e7982.

Sadler, M (2011). *Food, Glycaemic Response and Health*. Brussels, Belgium: ILSI Europe. p. 1-30.

Sampson, HA (2004) Food allergy. Part 1: immunopathogenesis and clinical disorders. *J Allergy Clin Immunol*, 113:805-819.

Sasano, H *et al.* (1989) Analysis of lectin binding in benign and malignant thyroid nodules. *Arch Pathol Lab Med*, 113(2):186-9.

Schernhammer, ES *et al.* (2005) Circulating levels of insulin-like growth factors, their binding proteins, and breast cancer risk. *Cancer Epidemiol Biomarkers Prev*, 14(3):699-704.

Simopoulos, AP (2008) The importance of the omega-6/omega-3 fatty acid ratio in cardiovascular disease and other chronic diseases. Exp Biol Med (Maywood), 233(6):674-88.

Sheard, NF *et al.* (2004) Dietary carbohydrate (amount and type) in the prevention and management of diabetes: a statement by the american diabetes association. *Diabetes Care*, 27 (9): 2266-71.

Sollid, LM *et al.* (1986) Antibodies to wheat germ agglutinin in coeliac disease. *Clin Exp Immunol*, 63(1): 95-100.

St-Onge, MP *et al.* (2003) Medium-chain triglycerides increase energy expenditure and decrease adiposity in overweight men. *Obes Res*, 11(3):395-402.

Swallow, D M (2003) Genetics of lactase persistence and lactose intolerance. *Annu Rev Genet,* 37: 197-219.

Tchernychev, B & Wilchek, M (1996) Natural human antibodies to dietary lectins. *FEBS Lett*, 18;397(2-3):139-42

Thomas, B (2001) *Manual of dietetic practice* (3rd ed). Oxford: Blackwell Science Ltd.

Travis, RC & Kay, TJ (2003) Oestrogen exposure and breast cancer risk. *Breast Cancer Res*, 5(5): 239-247.

Tseng, M *et al.* (2005) Dairy, calcium, and vitamin D intakes and prostate cancer risk in the National Health and Nutrition Examination Epidemiologic Follow-up Study cohort. *Am J Clin Nutr*, 81(5):1147-54.

Tucker, KL *et al.* (1999) Potassium, magnesium, and fruit and vegetable intakes are associated with greater bone mineral density in elderly men and women. *Am J Clin Nutr*, 69:727-736.

Ventura, A (2000) Gluten-dependent diabetes-related and thyroid-related autoantibodies in patients with celiac disease. *J. Pediatr,* 137(2):263-5.

Volpe, SL (2013) Magnesium in disease prevention and overall health. *Adv Nutr*, 1; 4(3):378S-83S.

Voskuil, DW *et al.* (2005) The insulin-like growth factor system in cancer prevention: potential of dietary intervention strategies. *Cancer Epidemiol Biomarkers Prev,* 14:195-203.

Walsh, WE (2000) *Food allergies*. New York: John Wiley & Sons.

Wang, Y *et al.* (1998) The genetically programmed down-regulation of lactase in children. *Gastroenterol,* 114 (6): 1230-6.

World Health Organization (1996) *Trace elements in human nutrition and health*. (http://whqlibdoc.who.int/publications/1996/9241561734_eng.pdf. Accessed: 6 June 2013).

Useful websites

Allergy UK:
www.allergyuk.org

American Diabetes Association:
www.diabetes.org

Australasian Society of Clinical Immunology and Allergy:
www.allergy.org.au/patients/food-other-adverse-reactions/food-intolerance

Canadian Celiac Association:
www.celiac.ca

Celiac Disease Center (Columbia University):
www.celiacdiseasecenter.columbia.edu

Coeliac UK:
www.coeliac.org.uk

Diabetes UK:
www.diabetes.org.uk

Environmental Working Group:
www.ewg.org/foodnews/summary.php

Glycemic Index Database (University of Sydney):
www.glycemicindex.com

Glycemic Research Institute:
www.glycemic.com

Health Concerns about Dairy Products (Physicians Committee for Responsible Medicine):
www.pcrm.org/health/diets/vegdiets/health-concerns-about-dairy-products

National Digestive Diseases Information Clearinghouse (NDDIC):
http://digestive.niddk.nih.gov

Nutrition Data:
http://nutritiondata.self.com

Simple Steps to Preventing Diabetes (Harvard School of Public Health):
www.hsph.harvard.edu/nutritionsource/diabetes-full-story

Wheat-free resources:
www.wheat-free.org

FREE
<u>ACHIEVE YOUR IDEAL WEIGHT</u>
self-hypnosis download

Dear Reader,
If you would like to claim your
free download, please email
eva@ttherapy.co.uk,
and write "free download"
in the subject box.

About the author

Eva Detko, PhD, started her therapy training 15 years ago. During this time she has worked with a wide range of clients, both in the UK and abroad. She has successfully supported people with weight problems, depression, anxiety, chronic pain, compromised immune function, as well as digestive, skin and cardiovascular conditions. Apart from treating individual clients, Dr Eva has worked as a health and fitness consultant for a number of Primary Care Trusts and voluntary sector organisations in the UK. She also has substantial health research and teaching experience.

Dr Eva's training is the field of human physiology and nutritional sciences is extensive, and includes: a doctorate degree in Physiology, Biochemistry and Nutrition, and a Master of Science degree in Human Nutrition. Dr Eva is also trained in clinical and medical hypnotherapy, and she is a Master Practitioner of Neuro-Linguistic Psychology.

Combining all her therapeutic knowledge, experience and skills enables Dr Eva to provide a truly groundbreaking approach to well-being, that helps clients target their health problems in a completely natural way. Dr Eva believes that each client requires an approach that reflects their biochemical, psychological and emotional individuality. She also believes that health is a function of many different factors, and it is important to balance all of these factors in order to achieve the state of optimal well-being.

Dr Eva is available for consultations via Skype. To find out more, visit
www.transformationtherapywiltshire.co.uk, or email: **eva@ttherapy.co.uk**